YORK NOTES

General Editors: Professor A
of Stirling) & Professor Suhe
University of Beirut)

Ernest Heming

THE OLD MAN AND THE SEA

Notes by Kenneth Graham
MA (GLASGOW), D PHIL (OXFORD)
Professor of English Literature, University of Sheffield

LONGMAN
YORK PRESS

We are grateful to the following for permission to reproduce copyright material:

Jonathan Cape Ltd and the Executors of the Ernest Hemingway Estate for extracts from *The Old Man and the Sea* by Ernest Hemingway.

YORK PRESS
Immeuble Esseily, Place Riad Solh, Beirut.

LONGMAN GROUP UK LIMITED
Longman House, Burnt Mill, Harlow,
Essex CM20 2JE, England
Associated companies, branches and representatives throughout the world

First published 1980
Sixth impression 1992

ISBN 0-582-78224-4

Printed in Hong Kong
WLEE/06

Contents

Part 1

Introduction

Hemingway's life

Ernest Hemingway was born in Oak Park, Illinois, just outside Chicago, in 1899 and died by suicide in Ketchum, Idaho, in 1961. His father was a doctor and his mother a former singer and teacher of music. The father cultivated the outdoor life of hunting and camping as an escape from the gentility and conventionality of his home life—and from the dominant cultured and religious standards of Hemingway's mother. It was from such a divided upbringing—not an uncommon one in many a country or time, and especially so in America—that Hemingway's own fondness for the 'masculine' life of sport and hardship developed. He rejected the possibility of college education after leaving school; and having been turned down on medical grounds for active service in the First World War, in 1917, he briefly became a newspaper reporter in Kansas City before enlisting as an ambulance driver with the Red Cross in Italy.

In 1918 he suffered his famous traumatic wound at the front, when an Austrian mortar shell exploded close to him and he was then hit in the leg by machine-gun fire while carrying a wounded man to safety. He spent three months in hospital in Milan, was awarded a medal, and had an unsuccessful love-affair: many of the details are recorded later in *A Farewell to Arms*, and the effect of the whole adventure lasted with him for life.

After this experience of sudden violence, slightly exaggerated heroics, and a bitter-sweet late-adolescent love, the next stage in Hemingway's career was his entry into the professional world of literature. After some time working as a reporter for the Toronto *Star* and as a journalist in Chicago, he married and, armed with letters of introduction from the successful writer Sherwood Anderson, set off for Paris. There, he lived the life of the American literary expatriate: experimenting with his first short fiction, talking, drinking, quarrelling, travelling, being much influenced and advised by Gertrude Stein, boxing with Ezra Pound, and in general making himself a very active member of the Parisian-American literary scene in what were its most creative and hectic years.

His first important work, the series of brilliant sketches and short stories called *In Our Time*, was published in New York in 1925, while *The Sun Also Rises* (published as *Fiesta* in Britain) became a best-seller in 1926 and firmly established his fame. This novel became a Bible of a whole generation (Gertrude Stein, Hemingway's fellow-novelist and mentor, called it 'a Lost Generation'), and began the cult of Hemingway and of supposed Hemingway attitudes: the attitudes of tight-lipped and stoical disillusionment in a world of senseless and sudden violence, the absence of faith but the cultivation of composure, the code of understatement, wry, sardonic wit, and a slightly self-pitying 'toughness'. His second major novel, *A Farewell to Arms*, in 1929, along with his continuing publication of short stories (collected as *Men Without Women* in 1927 and *Winner Take Nothing* in 1933), confirmed Hemingway's stature as one of the most influential prose-writers of the period.

Divorced, re-married, and living in Key West, Florida, on the proceeds of his fiction, Hemingway took up a hectic life of writing, reporting and travel; following bullfights (described in *Death in the Afternoon*, 1932), big-game-hunting in Africa (described in *Green Hills of Africa*, 1935), and consciously projecting a public image of almost mythic proportions. He acted as a war correspondent in the Spanish Civil War in 1937, supporting the Republican side but gaining freshly disillusioned insight into the muddle and injustice that afflicts both sides in any war. *For Whom the Bell Tolls*, in 1940, was the most notable result of his Spanish experiences.

Having divorced and re-married for a second time, and then again for a third time; having reported the war between China and Japan in 1941 and the Allied campaign in Europe in 1944 (where he did some unofficial fighting); Hemingway then began the final period of his career as a resident of Cuba, where he had bought a small estate. There, he continued his life of well-advertised hunting and adventure, being often in the forefront of literary publicity and controversy: still a figure of vitality, but increasingly adopting postures and therefore incurring hostile and even malicious criticism. An unsuccessful novel about an ageing but wistfully swaggering hero, *Across the River and into the Trees* (1950), dramatised the problems of Hemingway's later years. And only with *The Old Man and the Sea*, in 1952, did the author seem to rise with any triumph above the process of bad-tempered decline. That story was immediately successful, and was partly responsible for Hemingway's winning the Nobel Prize for Literature in 1954. After a bad plane crash in the same year, while on safari in Africa, Hemingway's health slowly worsened; and it was after having treatment for severe depression that he shot himself in 1961 in his house in Idaho.

The Hemingway world

The Old Man and the Sea, though it comes near the end of Hemingway's writing career, is in most ways a work characteristic of its author. And though it should be read for its own sake, and allowed to create its own 'world', it does also carry with it many suggestions that point outside itself, to the general view of life that Hemingway developed in the novels and stories that preceded it.

Through almost everything Hemingway wrote, there is a deep note of unease and instability. Something is being held at bay, and only just held at bay. Clearly, this proceeds from something in the personal psychology of the author; and even the barest outline of his life, such as has just been given above, is enough to suggest explanations of this deep-seated insecurity. But the feeling is not only personal and psychological. Hemingway is also able to locate it in something beyond himself: in his historical period, for example, the era of the 'Lost Generation', frenzied, careless, casually rich, hard-living. It is the era of the period between the two world wars, when one war has destroyed all the old social and intellectual stabilities of the nineteenth century, leaving nothing in their place, and the threat of the new war is almost immediately at hand. Hemingway's unease is that of the individual man, fearful for his own masculinity, oppressed by the need perpetually to prove himself. But this unease in his books is also that of Europe and America between the wars. And this representative quality helps to give his writings their power, and to make them far more significant than merely private outpourings could be.

The sense of threat is everywhere, and gives a strange, taut energy to Hemingway's writing. Fear energises his work, like a tight spring. *In Our Time*, his first book which some people think his finest, resembles T.S. Eliot's *The Waste Land* (1922) in the way it interweaves snatches of remembered experience, overheard voices, and brief pictures of futile modern living, so as to convey an overall impression of tension, breakdown, and impending catastrophe. Each of the short stories that comprise *In Our Time* is about violence, or betrayal, or weakness, and the figure of Nick Adams, who recurs in them, becomes the prototype of the Hemingway hero: initiated young into a hostile world, battered and scarred by his encounters with that world, and seen at the end (in the brilliant concluding story, 'Big Two-Hearted River') clinging desperately to the skills of fishing, alone in a dangerous landscape. And between each story—to drive the lesson home—occurs a small vignette from a scene of war, or bullfighting, or criminal violence. Even the structure of the book emphasises the fragmentariness of the twentieth century. There is no philosophical security here—no system, social or religious, is left—only lonely individuals doing a few brave or futile things before night falls. As in *The Old Man and the Sea*, it is a world of sharks: they wait till a man has achieved something, then they take it away from him. And all he can do under that threat is to concentrate on what is nearest at hand: the practical necessities of working, or tasting wine or coffee, or catching bait for his fishing. This is one positive thing in Hemingway's bleak view of life—bleaker in his early work than in his later—that one can at least enjoy some moments of sensuous experience, and take pride in the 'tricks' and skills of certain activities. But even in the memorable detail with which Hemingway's narration focuses so intensely on these simple things and acts, there is something feverish, something deliberately strained and neurotic.

The bullfighter becomes another significant figure in Hemingway's world, and is also in many ways a preparation for Santiago, the heroic fisherman who 'plays' his great fish with the patience and skill of the matador—and like the matador comes to 'love' his victim. The hero can be literally a bullfighter, like Pedro Romero in *The Sun Also Rises* and the real-life bullfighters of *Death in the Afternoon*, or he can be any man who enacts in life the bullfighter's performance: a man facing up squarely to the menace of existence and 'playing' it with coolness, irony, courage, and 'grace under pressure'. The latter phrase brings together a code of life and a code of art. The Hemingway hero meets the challenge of death and disaster by a code of behaviour that is supposed to have its own beauty. The code is one that forswears all rhetoric and displays of emotion, exactly as Hemingway's own artistic style tries to do. Those who show too much emotion and forget the rule of ironic nonchalance—like Robert Cohn in *A Farewell to Arms*—are the anti-heroes. They are 'messy', disruptive, and ineffectual. They are as bad as a bad bullfighter, who can only maim and not kill his bull cleanly. And they are as bad as a bad sentence or paragraph, that cannot form and shape the raw material it is trying to turn into art.

A mark of the heroic man, the man who follows the code, is not just that he meets the threat of chaos with an almost artistic 'manner' of speech and behaviour, but also that he bears the wounds inflicted by that outside hostile force. The physical pain and wounds of Santiago, in *The Old Man and the Sea*, have many predecessors in Hemingway's work. There is the crippled arm of Harry Morgan in *To Have and Have Not*, Frederic Henry's leg-wound in *A Farewell to Arms*, Jake Barnes's emasculating war-wound in *The Sun Also Rises*, Nick Adams's war-wound in *In Our Time*, and a psychological wound, such as Robert Jordan's memory of his father's suicide in *For Whom the Bell Tolls*.

Here is the theory of the wound as expressed by Frederic Henry himself in Chapter 34 of *A Farewell to Arms*:

> If people bring so much courage to this world the world has to kill them to break them, so of course it kills them. The world breaks every one and afterward many are strong at the broken places. But those that will not break it kills. It kills the very good and the very gentle and the very brave impartially. If you are none of these you can be sure it will kill you too but there will be no special hurry.

The wound represents the point where the 'world', everything that is hostile and uncontrollable in existence, meets the individual man and puts him to the test. It is a badge of endurance and of knowledge. He must take his wound with 'grace' under the breaking 'pressure' of life. To do so allows him new strength to get through the rest of life, though as soon as he infringes the 'code' he has forgotten his lesson and loses his worth. No matter what happens, the 'world' will get him in the end.

Hemingway's is a very black view—so black that the reader is reminded not only of the era of T.S. Eliot (1888–1965) and Franz Kafka (1883–1924) (and Samuel Beckett (*b.*1906) after them), but of the Jacobean era in English literature, when tragic dramatists such as John Webster (1580–1625) and Cyril Tourneur (1575–1626) saw around them a blank inexplicable universe of depravity and sudden death, and like Hemingway saw the only possible response as one that cultivated stoicism, cold wit, and ironic resignation. Hemingway's famous short story 'A Clean, Well-Lighted Place' (1933), provides one of his most concise expressions of this near-nihilism, in its image of life as a place of *Nada*, dark nothingness, which a man can keep at bay only temporarily, by seeking refuge in the clean well-lighted place of the cafe, until he is forced to leave and contemplate despair once again (night is always a bad time for the early Hemingway heroes, who often need to sleep with the light on).

In such a world, what is needed most of all is 'luck', and one must try to 'buy' luck (again like Santiago) by accepting some misfortune and pain. 'Thinking' too much is as dangerous as sleeping without the light on, since thought can lead only to the revelation that there is no sense to the world. And love for a woman is almost as dangerous, since it leads to commitment to another, and therefore to doubling the chances of suffering and loss. Hemingway's is essentially a male world, where women offer brief episodes of happiness and companionship, but in the end only emphasise the essential loneliness of a man. To survive, a man has to keep himself to himself, give away very little, and develop a self-defensive style of detachment. He must limit himself, and like the matador offer to the enemy—the bull—not a full view of himself, but only what he chooses to offer.

Against nihilism and self-limitation, Hemingway does hold up more positive things. There is the code itself; and certain human values, notably those of endurance, courage, and compassion, are always glorified by him—especially in his later, less despairing work, from *For Whom the Bell Tolls* to *The Old Man and the Sea*. And even in the early work, Hemingway believes with intensity that certain things in life are real and valuable: vital things like objects, places, weather, the flavour of wine, or the excitement of casting for trout. Among the most memorable things in Hemingway's writings are his various evocations of such 'positive' elements in the way we live. This delight in the transient things of the world is a counterweight, philosophically, to his view of the world's essential emptiness or hostility. And it is also very important artistically. We do not turn to art directly for its philosophical insights, but in the first place for the pleasure it gives us. And Hemingway's writings are firmly rescued from the dangers of a vague, philosophic gloom by the extraordinary vividness with which they re-create events and experiences. His writing is given intensity and variety by the way it seizes on the things of the world—like this:

> In the late summer of that year we lived in a house in a village that looked across the river and the plain to the mountains. In the bed of the river there were pebbles and boulders, dry and white in the sun, and the water was clear and swiftly moving and blue in the channels. Troops went by the house and down the road and the dust they raised powdered the leaves of the trees. The trunks of the trees too were dusty and the leaves fell early that year and we saw the troops marching along the road and the dust rising and leaves, stirred by the breeze, falling and the soldiers marching and afterwards the road bare and white except for the leaves.

It is only on reflection and re-reading that we begin also to 'interpret' such a passage—the famous first paragraph from *A Farewell to Arms*—and to find in it patterns of significance and even of symbolism. But without that immediate sense of colour and texture and movement and seasons of the year, the passage would not have its full significance, and certainly would not provide us with the full pleasure that art requires.

And lastly, to set against the impending darkness of Hemingway's view of the world, there is his sense of *idyll*: that is, of simple peace and perfection. As well as being disenchanted and pessimistic, Hemingway is a romantic. He has—contradictorily, perhaps—a brief dream of paradise as well as a vision of hell. Paradise is very brief for him; but it is vivid while it lasts, or while it is imagined and desired. It is usually away from the main action: an expedition or a dream. But it is so accurately reported that it becomes real, and it serves to highlight and qualify all the rest of the action. Take, for example, the trip to fish for trout in the ice-cold Irati River, in *The Sun Also Rises*, where the two men keep their wine cool in the stream, pack the fine firm trout they catch in layers of fresh ferns, and talk happily and wittily. Or the various evocations of the distant region of the Abruzzi, in *A Farewell to Arms*, 'where it was clear cold and dry and the snow was dry and powdery and hare-tracks in the snow and the peasants took off their hats and called you Lord and there was good hunting'. All around may be the fatuousness of war, the vast universal chaos of chance and betrayal; but somewhere in Hemingway's world there is always a dream, like Santiago's, of innocent lions gambolling on a dazzling white beach. These are the hidden places of our imaginative and emotional life: the places that strengthen us in our struggles. And they are the places, too, from which comes the artist's urge to create.

Hemingway's world is partly determined by Hemingway's vision of his art. And it is the life-long seriousness of his dedication to words and to form that offers the most convincing evidence that he was no bleak nihilist but only a pessimist who loved the things that time always takes away from us. He shaped and revised and experimented with words to the end of his life. His style, so concrete, so hostile to abstraction and rhetoric, is his own. But it stands close to the central preoccupations of the Modern Movement in literature in the second and third decades of this century. Like the changes in poetic style enforced by Ezra Pound (1885–1972), T.S. Eliot, Robert Frost (1874–1963), and William Carlos Williams (1883–1963), and like the prose of Gertrude Stein (1874–1946) and the verbal intricacies of James Joyce (1882–1941), it was an attempt to refine away all falsity through enigmatic ironies, compression, and self-conscious detachment. Impersonality became a catchword, and while easier to talk of than to achieve in practice (in more cases than Hemingway's), it stood for a reaction against the old romanticism and Victorianism, and marked the cult of a new would-be classicism in letters. In fact Hemingway is more of a romantic than he would have liked to think. But the 'hard edge' of his language, and its effect of cool but intense precision, combined with his sardonic and disillusioned view of life, keeps him firmly among the moderns. He has the authentic modern imagination of violence and disorder. And he is kept somewhere in the vicinity of modern giants like Joyce and Eliot and Thomas Mann (1873–1955)—though far below them in actual achievement—by the way he took art itself as a high endeavour and as a bulwark against nothingness and despair. Hemingway wrote much that was inferior, but some things that were true and lasting, *The Old Man and the Sea* being one of them. In the end, for all his pessimism, the seriousness with which he took literature is a token of the seriousness with which he took life—our own unsteady, unilluminated modern life. And in that seriousness, as in other ways too, he is like one of his own heroes: a wounded, imperfect, but genuine hero of art.

A source for *The Old Man and the Sea*

The main events of the story seem to have been based on a real incident, described by Hemingway in an article about fishing in the Gulf Stream in *Esquire* for April 1936:

> Another time an old man fishing alone in a skiff out of Cabañas hooked a great marlin that, on the heavy sashcord handline, pulled the skiff far out to sea. Two days later the old man was picked up by fishermen sixty miles to the eastward, the head and forward part of the marlin lashed alongside. What was left of this fish, less than half, weighed eight hundred pounds. The old man had stayed with him a day, a night, a day and another night while the fish swam deep and pulled the boat. When he had come up the old man had pulled the boat up on him and harpooned him. Lashed alongside the sharks had hit him and the old man had fought them out alone in the Gulf Stream in a skiff, clubbing them, stabbing at them, lunging at them with an oar until he was exhausted and the sharks had eaten all that they could hold. He was crying in the boat when the fishermen picked him up, half crazy from his loss, and the sharks were still circling the boat.

Though it is far from certain, the original old man may have been Anselmo Hernandez, a local fisherman who was known to Hemingway and who made the claim after Hemingway's death.

A note on the text

There are no textual problems about *The Old Man and the Sea*. It was first published in *Life* for September 1952, and immediately afterwards that same month in book-form by Charles Scribner's Sons, of New York. It has been reprinted many times. There are at present hardback and paperback editions in print by Scribner's, New York, 1952, and in Great Britain, by Jonathan Cape, London, 1952; and there is a paperback edition by Panther Books, St. Albans, 1976.

In Part 2 page references are shown for the Jonathan Cape edition.

Part 2

Summaries
of THE OLD MAN AND THE SEA

General summary

Santiago, an old Cuban fisherman who has gone eighty-four days without catching a fish, at last hooks an eighteen-foot marlin, the largest he has ever known. The fish is too powerful for Santiago, who now fishes alone having lost the help of the boy, Manolin, who used to sail with him. For forty-eight hours it tows him and his boat out to sea, with Santiago bearing the whole weight of the fish by the line around his back. The old man, with little sleep or food, endures much pain; but on his third day at sea, after heroic efforts, he succeeds in drawing the weakened marlin to the surface, and harpoons it. The fish is so big that it cannot be pulled into the boat, and has to be lashed alongside. And so, while the exhausted Santiago sails back to harbour, his catch is exposed to the sharks, who attack it all night, despite his desperate defence. By the time he reaches shore only the giant skeleton of the marlin is left. The old man struggles to his shack, having lost what he fought for and won; but his struggle has brought him respect.

Detailed summaries

The Old Man and the Sea is a *novella*, that is, a long short story, and is not divided into chapters or numbered sections. One useful way of remembering and of summarising its action is in terms of its time-scheme. What follows should be seen as a mere framework to help the reader to remember and understand more clearly its full structure and meaning. All summaries debase the work in question; and to summarise is also to begin to interpret and extract meaning. So any summary you yourself might make could well be different in several respects from the one offered now.

The glossary of words and phrases that follows each time-section has been kept to a minimum; some words are explained in the course of the summary. Words such as 'skiff' or 'thwart' that can be looked up easily in a dictionary have been omitted, as well as words such as 'salao' or 'guano' or 'Hatuey beer' that are sufficiently explained or made clear in the context of the story, or some geographical allusions which do not need to be pursued in detail.

The evening before *(pp.5–22,Cape edition)*

Each time that Santiago sails in his skiff into harbour from another day's unsuccessful fishing, he is met by the boy, Manolin, who helps him carry his fishing gear ashore: the lines, the harpoon, and the gaff for landing the fish. The boy had been his companion at sea until his long run of bad luck made the boy's parents place him in another, luckier, fishing boat. The old man, whose appearance is almost as dilapidated as his boat, still loves the boy, and sits with him at the Terrace, the local bar, drinking beer among the other fishermen.

Santiago and Manolin talk, with affection and with hope, about the past and about the future. Manolin remembers when Santiago once went eighty-seven days without a catch, then was successful. Since his parents will not allow him to fish with Santiago, he offers to help by catching sardines for Santiago to use as bait. They remember the times they have spent together, and their adventures at sea. Manolin hopes to persuade his skipper, despite the latter's poor vision, to fish far out next day, so that they can be near Santiago's boat if he should need some help.

When they reach Santiago's primitive shack, Manolin enquires about the old man's dinner, and is answered (as he is every day) by the polite and dignified fiction that he has a pot of rice with fish. Knowing that he has no food, Manolin will later on bring Santiago a meal from the Terrace. They talk of the American baseball matches, then of their idea of buying a ticket for the lottery. Santiago sleeps in his chair while Manolin goes off to catch the sardines. He makes sure the old man eats, and they talk of their baseball heroes, such as Joe DiMaggio and Dick Sisler, and of famous baseball managers, like John J. McGraw and Leo Durocher, who had actually visited the Terrace in the past. Santiago arranges to waken the boy at his home in the morning (he does not like being wakened by his new skipper), and they part.

Santiago, asleep on his simple bed, dreams, as he often does, of when he sailed to Africa on a sailing-ship as a boy, and saw lions come down and play like cats on the beach.

NOTES AND GLOSSARY:

the Gulf Stream: a major sea-current that flows eastwards off the north coast of Cuba

Santiago: the name means Saint James, a central figure in the traditions of Spanish (and Latin-American) Catholicism, and himself a fisherman

ice truck . . . the market in Havana: the fish are transported by refrigerated truck to Havana, the capital of Cuba

I brought the fish in too green: the fish was brought in before it had tired itself, and still fresh

I will see something that he cannot see such as a bird working and get him to come out after dolphin: Manolin will pretend to his near-blind skipper that he sees a bird swooping further out at sea, signifying the presence of a school of dolphin, and in that way he will trick him into taking the boat out towards Santiago's

a picture in colour of the Sacred Heart of Jesus and another of the Virgin of Cobre: typical pious pictures to be found in any poor Catholic home in Cuba. The Virgin of Cobre is a sacred figure particularly worshipped on the island

bring one in that dressed out over a thousand pounds: a fish that weighed over a thousand pounds even after being gutted and trimmed

bodega: a bar or food shop

The Yankees cannot lose . . .: part of the half-humorousness of the baseball references, especially for American readers, lies in the fact that the teams are properly called the Cleveland Indians, for example, and not the Indians of Cleveland. The others are the New York Yankees (for whom DiMaggio played), the Cincinnati Reds, and the Chicago White Sox (signifying 'socks'). The equivalent in humorousness for the English reader, say, would be this: 'I fear both the United of Manchester and the Villa of Aston'

Qué va: 'not so' or 'not at all'

The first day *(pp.22–44)*

Santiago wakens in the cold darkness of the hour before dawn and, having wakened the boy, walks with him to the harbour among the other fishermen. They drink coffee, divide up their baits, and Manolin pushes out the old man's skiff. Santiago rows steadily out to sea until he is alone—except that he is never alone on a sea populous with flying fish and terns.

Santiago thinks of the beauty and cruelty of the sea, and of how he looks on the sea as a woman, fickle and desirable, but how others—especially the younger fishermen, eager for money—think of the sea as masculine, and as an opponent. While he keeps an eye open for signs of the schools of tuna (sometimes called bonita or albacore) where the marlin might be found feeding, he carefully sets his lines, each at a different depth, the hooks baited on the shank with a larger fish, like tuna or blue runner or yellow jack, and on the point with small fresh sardines. Every detail of hook, bait, and line is given his full attention, and his lines always hang straighter and more precisely at their depth than any other fisherman's.

Two hours after sunrise, Santiago spots his first school of dolphin (or dorado), recognising their presence by the flurry of flying fish trying to escape them and by the sight of a man-of-war bird trying to catch the flying fish. He hopes a marlin is in the vicinity, and in the meantime tries to catch a dolphin for an extra bait.

He sees the clouds of plankton in the water (promising the presence of fish, drawn to their natural food), the floating Sargasso weed, and (what he always hates and curses) the jellyfish-like Portuguese man-of-war, which looks beautiful as it drifts like a coloured bubble, but with its deadly sting is 'the falsest thing in the sea'. Santiago thinks of how he loves to see turtles eating the men-of-war, and then, with affection, of all the habits of the turtle. He has hunted turtle and eaten their eggs (just as he drinks some shark liver oil every day for his health); but always has felt sorry for the turtles, and sympathises with them in their suffering.

Now Santiago sights a school of small tuna, helped by the man-of-war bird again; and just then he catches a tuna on one of the short bait-lines. He pulls the ten-pound fish in and hits him on the head quickly, 'for kindness', speaking his thoughts aloud as he has now got into the habit of doing. It is noon. The sun is becoming hot, and he resists the temptation to sleep. It is his eighty-fifth day without a catch, and he must fish well.

At this instant, the marker-stick on one of his lines dips, and Santiago knows that a marlin, a hundred fathoms (that is, six hundred feet) down, is nibbling at the bait. Holding the line carefully Santiago speaks aloud encouragingly, then as the line suddenly uncoils through his fingers he knows the marlin has taken the bait. He prepares his lines, waiting for the marlin to eat the bait; then suddenly 'strikes' with both hands, to lodge the hook securely in the fish's gullet. The fish is so heavy that Santiago cannot pull it in even by an inch, and it begins to tow the fisherman in his boat. He cannot tie the rope fast to the boat lest the fish suddenly snap the line: he must himself take the strain, and let out a little more line when necessary.

The skiff moves off steadily to the north-west, out of sight of land, with the old man taking the terrible strain of the rope across his back. He waits for the fish to come to the surface; but all he can do now is to drink a little, and settle as best as he can to wait and to endure.

NOTES AND GLOSSARY:

Agua mala . . . you whore: literally, 'evil water'. The Portuguese man-of-war's combination of beauty and corruption makes Santiago see it as a prostitute

carapaced: the carapace is the hard upper shell of the turtle

green turtles and hawks-bills . . . logger-heads . . . trunk-backs: different types of turtle

grippes: influenza

I'm the towing bitt: the bitt is a deck-post for fastening ropes or cables

if he sounds: if he dives

The first night *(pp.44–51)*

All night the marlin pursues the same course. Santiago protects his shoulders a little by an old sack, and he leans against the bow, but does not sleep. The glow in the sky from Havana is fading as the current takes both of them—the tower and the towed—towards the east. He wishes he had the boy with him to help; and reminds himself to eat the tuna he caught in the morning, to preserve his strength. He hears porpoises playing; and thinks with interest and pity of the marlin, wondering whether, like himself, it is desperate.

He remembers an incident that had saddened him in the past, when a male marlin would not leave the female after Santiago and Manolin had hooked her, and leaped high out of the water to see his mate lying in Santiago's boat before swimming away alone. He thinks of the strange fate that has joined him and the fish together: they are linked by the consequences of individual choice and of chance.

Before dawn, a fish takes one of his bait lines, and with one free hand he has to cut the line quickly, to conserve rope. He joins together all the reserve rope he has; pausing once again to wish he had the boy with him.

At one point, the marlin makes a sudden lunge, pulling Santiago down on his face and cutting it. He wonders if the fish's back, like his, has felt the pain of the rope. He vows to stay with the fish to the end; and knows the fish will stay with him. He huddles against the wood of the boat to keep warm; and when the sun rises the fish is still swimming strongly, to the north.

NOTES AND GLOSSARY:

the rapier bill: the marlin, like a swordfish, has its upper jaw projecting into a sword-like weapon

The second day *(pp.51–73)*

The marlin, though untired, is swimming less deeply. Santiago hopes it will soon jump above the surface, since in that case the air taken into the sacs along its spine will prevent it going down so deeply again.

A small land-bird, a warbler, lands on the line to rest from its flight over the sea. Santiago speaks whimsically and affectionately to the bird, thinking that it, like him, and like the fish, has a hard time coming when it approaches the hawks waiting near the land. Suddenly, the marlin gives another surge, pulling Santiago down, and cutting his right hand. He regrets his inattention, longs for the boy again, washes the blood from his hand, and slowly makes himself eat the tuna. As he does so, he is disgusted to find that his left hand is cramped, and speaks to it reprovingly and encouragingly. He will need both hands whenever the marlin—which he now calls his 'brother'—comes to the surface.

He looks round at the sea and appreciates all that is moving and living on it. He sees wild ducks, and reads the signs of the weather in the clouds. Suddenly, while he is still trying to free his hand from cramp, the line rises and the marlin leaps out of the water, 'unendingly'. Santiago, preoccupied with controlling one-handed the uncoiling line as the fish dives, realises it is the biggest marlin he has ever seen, two feet longer than the boat itself.

The marlin settles, and does not jump again. Santiago wonders if he jumped to show how big he was; and hopes he can show the marlin how much of a man he is. By noon, his treacherous left hand is uncramped. He promises to make a pilgrimage to the Virgin of Cobre if he catches the marlin, and says some prayers automatically, before turning again to practicalities and planning to bait a line to catch a fish to eat. He must have strength to kill the great marlin and prove (for what the narrator tells us is the thousandth time) that he is indeed, as he told Manolin, 'a strange old man'. He tells himself to rest and not to think; but still he imagines the movements of the fish down in the darkness, and finds his mind turning to the baseball games being played, many hundreds of miles away, in the States. Joe DiMaggio is his hero: the son of a fisherman, a man who does what he has to do perfectly, and who suffers from the perpetual pain and disadvantage of a 'bone spur', an irregular growth in the bone of the heel. Santiago, in his own pain, hopes he will be worthy of his hero.

He tries to strengthen his spirits by remembering how he won a game of hand-wrestling years ago against the strongest man in the docks. For a day and night the one hand of each was gripped tight against the other. Bets had been placed on the result, under the lamplights in the tavern room. And at daylight Santiago had forced the arm of the other flat on the table. He became *El Campeon*, the Champion.

He watches a plane pass overhead in the direction of Miami, and he wonders how the sea and how the fish would look from so high. He remembers with curiosity all the varied markings on the backs of fish, and how they look from a mast-head. Then, just before dark, his bait-line is taken by a dolphin, which he draws in and kills with his left hand.

It is sunset, 'a difficult time for all fish', and Santiago does not wish to disturb his marlin at such an hour. He imagines it must be weakening, and he sees it has slowed. Santiago has gone almost beyond pain, but he has confidence: he has food, his legs are strong. And he settles for the night, against the wood of the bow.

NOTES AND GLOSSARY:

rigor mortis: (*Latin*) the rigidity of a dead body

cumulus . . . cirrus: different cloud-formations

brisa: (*Spanish*) breeze

ptomaine poisoning: a form of food poisoning

juegos: (*Spanish*) games

Un espuela de hueso: Santiago, puzzled by this medical expression 'bone spur', simply repeats the phrase literally (in Spanish)

I'll lash the two oars together: Santiago plans to tie two oars outside the boat as a drag in the water, thereby tiring the fish

The second night *(pp.73–85)*

Santiago sees the first stars, 'his distant friends', and thinks of the fish, in all its dignity, as the friend and brother whom he must kill. He hesitates over the plan to make a drag from the oars, and decides it is safer not to do so: the fish, which has still much strength left, would be able to pull too much line from a slower-moving boat. He tries to pass on as much of the strain of the fish as he can to the boat itself, and decides he must try to sleep for a little while—since even the stars and the sun and the moon have to sleep.

First, he has to gut and eat the newly-caught dolphin, and he has the luck to find inside the dolphin two flying fish, still fresh and edible. As before, he regrets that he has no salt or lemon to make the raw fish palatable. He sees weather-signs—cloud obscuring the stars in the east—that indicate bad weather, but not for three or four days. Then he arranges his body so that the line will be held even though he sleeps.

He has various dreams, and has begun to dream happily of Africa and the lions when he is awakened rudely by the line rushing out through his hands, burning and cutting them as it goes. The fish is jumping out of the sea, unseen in the darkness, and the old man is pulled tightly against the bow. The crisis is at hand.

Slowly, Santiago begins to check the rushing line, and he knows the fish has jumped so often it has filled its air sacs and will soon begin to circle the boat in its last effort. He lets his torn right hand hang in the sea to stop it bleeding, and sees that the fish, tired, has begun to move to the east, letting the current help it. Santiago worries about his hands, especially the unreliable left hand. He eats the remaining flying fish as a final preparation for the struggle, and as the sun rises for the third time since he left harbour he sees that the fish has begun its circle.

NOTES AND GLOSSARY:

vent . . . maw: the vent is where the fish excretes; the maw is its gullet

phosphorus: the particles come from the skin of the fish, and are luminous in the darkness

there was a norther . . . and his right arm was asleep: Santiago (as often happens) transfers to a dream what he is also experiencing in reality: that is, coldness and loss of circulation in the arm holding the line, on which his body has to rest. A norther is a north wind

The third day *(pp.85–115)*

For two hours the fish circles, and Santiago, dizzy by now with exhaustion, keeps pulling in line when he can and letting it out when he has to. The fish is rising, and the circles are becoming closer. The marlin begins to hit with its sword against the wire leader that connects the hook to the line, and Santiago prays that it will not jump again in its desperation and thereby force the hook out of its mouth. The man and the fish are both fighting to control their agony.

Still the circling goes on, and still the line has to be pulled in, as Santiago struggles not to faint. At last, the fish surfaces, and Santiago painstakingly pulls it closer and closer, trying to get the fish on to its side. It has almost become a case of which of the two will succumb first. Time after time, the old man nearly succeeds in turning the fish; each time it rights itself and swims tiredly away. But with one last crippling effort Santiago gets the marlin on its side close to the boat, and with his last ounce of energy drives his harpoon into the fish's side. It leaps once, with a crash of spray; and is dead.

Even now, there is labour. Santiago has to lash the fish's body alongside the boat, marvelling at the size and weight of his catch, and proud of what he has done. He can hardly estimate the market value of the catch (it seems to be about $300). He raises his mast and sail, and boat and fish begin to sail together back towards the land.

Santiago, at last freed from the burden of the line, steers the boat, and begins to come back to reality from what now seems like a dream. He refreshes himself with a little of his water supply, and eats some small shrimps he finds in a patch of passing seaweed. He tends his hands, tries to keep his head clear, and wonders whether he is bringing in the fish or whether his brother, whom he has tricked into death, is bringing him.

Then starts the last act of the drama.

After an hour's sailing the first shark attacks, drawn by the presence of the marlin's blood in the water. He is a killer, with eight rows of double-edged teeth, and the old man, seeing him, knows he has no hope. But he will fight to the last. The shark hits the marlin, ripping out forty pounds of flesh at one blow. But Santiago hits him with his harpoon in just the right place, and the shark, taking the harpoon with him, sinks out of sight.

Santiago feels as though it is his own body, rather than the marlin's, that has been mutilated. He wishes now that he had never caught the marlin. But still he will not easily be defeated, and sails on stubbornly, taking pride in how he struck the shark, wondering if DiMaggio would have admired the blow, and waiting for the next shark to be drawn by the fresh blood from the marlin.

He prepares a weapon by tying a knife to one of the oars, and tries to hope. The idea that it is sinful to lose hope comes to him, and he wonders if it was a sin to kill the fish. But he is a fisherman—it is priests who are paid to think about sin, he thinks. A fisherman must do what he was born to do. He tries to ignore the idea of sin, but his nature makes him think, and he wonders if the fact that he loved the marlin even as he killed it will take away any sinfulness from the deed. Besides, everything kills everything else, he reflects.

Then comes the next attack. Two shovel-nosed sharks, hungry scavengers of the sea, tear at the body of the marlin, and with great difficulty, and agony from his torn hands, the old man manages to kill both with his improvised weapon. He cannot bear to look at what is left of the marlin, and apologises to it. Then he prepares for the next encounter, soaking his bleeding hands in the sea, where the blood from the marlin is now enough to attract sharks from far and wide.

Santiago similarly kills the next shark, but the knife snaps as he does so. And when the next pair of sharks arrive, just before sunset, he has only his wooden club left. He strikes and strikes at them till they are both driven off, but by now only half of the fish is left, and there is still no sight of land as the light fades.

NOTES AND GLOSSARY:

trade wind: prevailing wind (good for 'trade'), here from north-east to south-west. Santiago is by now well to the north-east of his home

Dentuso: Cuban dialect meaning large-toothed or sharp-toothed

San Pedro: Saint Peter, like Saint James, a famous fisherman

Galanos: Cuban dialect for brown-and-white spotted cattle, here used contemptuously

The third night *(pp.115–22)*

Santiago waits to see the glow in the sky from Havana, and thinks of how people in his town will be worrying about his absence. He speaks apologetically again to what is left of the fish, and imagines it joining him in battle against the sharks, their mutual enemy. He tries to revive some hope—hope that he might have some luck at the last, and bring in some part of the fish. But at midnight, as the lights of Havana begin to appear, the sharks attack in a pack. Santiago fights them in the darkness with his club, till he loses it. Then he takes out the boat's tiller and fights them with that till it breaks. Then it is finished. The sharks have gone; there is nothing of the fish left for them to eat.

Wearily, without thoughts or feelings, save the thought that he 'went out too far' and dared too much, Santiago steers the skiff towards the land. Totally exhausted, he lands on the shingle of the deserted harbour, and is faced with his final physical task. In the darkness, he must carry his mast up the hill to his shack. He climbs and falls; then climbs and falls again, and again. Then, in his shack at last, he collapses on to the bed.

NOTES AND GLOSSARY:

a strange taste in his mouth: presumably, he is bleeding internally

The morning after *(pp.122–7)*

Manolin finds the old man asleep in the morning, and cries when he sees the condition of his hands. The weather has become rough, and the fishermen, not at sea, are all gathered wonderingly round Santiago's skiff in the harbour, measuring the enormous skeleton of the marlin.

Manolin fetches coffee from the Terrace, and gives it to Santiago when he wakens. The two of them talk of the adventure, and of the future. Manolin announces he will now disobey his parents and sail again with Santiago. They plan to replace the lost harpoon and knife. Manolin tells the old man to rest and get well, for he wishes to learn much from him. Santiago will give the marlin's bill to Manolin, and the head to Pedrico, the friendly shop-keeper.

In the afternoon, a woman in a group of tourists at the Terrace asks about the skeleton of the marlin lying in the water and misunderstands the waiter's reply. Ironically, she and her friend think it is a shark.

And meanwhile, in his shack, Santiago is asleep again, with Manolin watching over him. He is dreaming his dream of Africa and the lions.

NOTES AND GLOSSARY:

spring leaf from an old Ford: a strip of steel from the suspension of a scrapped Ford car

Tiburon: shark. The waiter, speaking in halting English ('Eshark' for 'shark'), means to tell the tourists how the marlin was reduced to a skeleton, but they think he is naming the fish itself

Part 3

Commentary

A caution

The Old Man and the Sea is a book that offers some temptations to the reader, the main one being the temptation to read too much into it. Critic after critic has discussed this short work as though it was Homer's *Iliad* or Shakespeare's *King Lear*, finding in it detailed Christian allegory, profound examination of the problems of evil and suffering, Existentialism, the quest for the Holy Grail, a parable of the heroic endeavour of the artist, and so on. It is often too easy to extract and then to parade 'themes' from a work of literature. And it is tempting for a student, eager to impress, to make a story sound like an essay in philosophy rather than an imitation of human character and human actions. What we have here is in no way a trivial story; but it would be wrong to overload it with solemn meanings. Hemingway wrote (in Chapter 16 of *Death in the Afternoon*):

> a serious writer is not to be confounded with a solemn writer. A serious writer may be a hawk or a buzzard or even a popinjay, but a solemn writer is always a bloody owl

There have been too many owls among critics and interpreters of Hemingway. And too much that is abstract or moral or philosophical has been heaped on to what is essentially a brilliantly simple and precise fiction. We would do well to begin by looking at what is most serious, as opposed to what is only most solemn, in *The Old Man and the Sea*: that is, what gives it realism and vitality as a narrative.

Realism

'I tried to make a real old man, a real boy, a real sea and a real fish and real sharks'*. That was how Hemingway described his own intentions in writing this story—or some of them at least. And most readers would at once agree he has succeeded. 'Realism' is of course a very difficult concept once we stop to examine it. It does not mean, 'that which we know might have happened in life exactly as the writer tells it'; although the events the 'realist' writer describes cannot be too far removed from actual possibility. And 'realism' also cannot mean 'that

**Time*, 13 December 1954

which is backed up by a great display of facts, measurements, and details', or 'that which is exactly like a photograph'. If so dangerously vague a word as 'realism' has any usefulness at all for literary criticism, it probably means something like this: 'a description that does not stray *too* far from what actually happens in life, and gives a certain amount of precise detail; but also, and above all, a description that uses selection and a closely-focussed intensity of imagining on the writer's part to *force* the reader to share in the events described'. That is, 'realism' such as Hemingway's is created by a degree of everyday normality and detail, but without imaginative *power* it cannot exist. In this way, literary 'realism' is different from a photograph, and can be said to extract the inner 'truth' from events rather than merely cataloguing their surfaces.

This is what Hemingway meant when he said that a writer's 'standard of fidelity to the truth should be so high that his invention, out of his experience, should produce a truer account than anything factual can be'*. And Hemingway's old man, boy, sea, fish, and sharks are not so much built up in our minds, detail by detail, fact by fact, as driven *into* our minds by the force and the sympathy with which the author himself shares in their imaginary existence. Like any realist, he relies on selection—choosing only a few details of colour or sound or taste, for example, that will concentrate our attention, and not let us be distracted by too many details. Without selection there can be no intensity, no compression. And without intensity there can be no 'realism'.

Now you should ask yourself whether the foregoing seems to you an adequate account of what 'realism' means, and how the effect of it is produced. Having thought of some other works of literature that strike you as being particularly 'realistic', you should draw up a list of the qualities that make them so. Can you think of some major works of literature that do not appear to be 'realistic', and what features do they have that are different from those of works of 'realism'?

It will be useful to list some examples of the striking *facts* we are given in this story about, for example, the habits of fish; the technique of catching marlin; the weather; the sea. Then show *why* Hemingway selects those particular facts at that particular point in the action.

Appeal to the senses

Consider how we are made to participate in the narrative of *The Old Man and the Sea* by Hemingway appealing to our various senses, exciting them, drawing them into the action.

*'Introduction' to *Men at War*, Crown Publishers, New York 1942, p.xv.

Taste, for example: the taste of beans and rice, with fried bananas and stew; the taste of hot coffee out of a condensed-milk tin in the hour before dawn; the foul (but health-giving) taste of shark-liver oil in a cup; the excessive sweetness of raw dolphin; the fine lack of stringiness in the taste of good marlin-flesh; the crunch of eating tiny shrimps in their shells; the tantalising absence in the mouth of lemon juice; and the sudden, sweet, coppery taste of a man's own blood. No one knows tastes better than Hemingway. They come like little bursts of energy throughout the progress of the narrative.

The use of *colour* is equally superb: effective not only because corresponding images of colour are at once evoked in our own visual imaginations, but because we are made to feel confidence in a writer who has such an accurate sense of the surfaces of the world. Our sense of 'realism', which is our sense of belief, can only be created by confidence. We must be persuaded by such things that such a writer, and therefore such a train of events, can be believed in. The use of colour, like the use of taste, is never excessive, and is used with economy, and always with a sense of how colours shift and change in their relationship. Too many colours in a description, or colours that are static, cancel themselves out, and draw attention only to a writer's desire to impress or to decorate. Sargasso weed is bleached and yellow by day. The Portuguese man-of-war trails long purple filaments. Tuna are silver when they jump out of the water, but blue-backed and gold-sided when swimming. A dolphin looks green when seen from a mast-head, but is really golden – except when dead, and at night, when it is 'a leprous grey-white'. And when the giant marlin finally surfaces, his tail 'was higher than a big scythe blade and a very pale lavender above the dark blue water'.

Light and dark are played off beautifully against one another, and, like night against day, add to the drama and the tensions of the action. There is a tell-tale glow in the sky from the lights of Havana; the phosphorescence of the floating weed at night; and the tiny bright particles of phosphorus floating away when the old man washes fish-scales from his hands in the sea.

Look at how Hemingway modulates his colours in this one example with the skill of a watercolour painter:

> The clouds over the land now rose like mountains and the coast was only a long green line with the grey-blue hills behind it. The water was a dark blue now, so dark that it was almost purple. As he looked down into it he saw the red sifting of the plankton in the dark water and the strange light the sun made now. (p.32)

We move from green to grey-blue to dark blue to 'almost purple' to red. Nothing clashes, because each of these colours is related to the colour that is next to it. Hemingway cleverly refrains from introducing the white of the mountain-like clouds. And when he ends with the unspecified 'strange light' of the sun, we can see and feel its strangeness, composed as it must be not just of all the colours that the sunlight has brought out, but of the very presence of movement, change, and revelation.

Perhaps the evocation of *touch* is the most miraculous of all, the one that draws us most completely *into* the action. (*Query*: or is the sense of picture and colour closer to our minds, and more important for this story? The reader should consider this for himself.) A story that emphasises physical suffering, on Santiago's part, needs this sense of touch. The story of the old fisherman stresses the simple, physical acts of life. The pain of the ropes across his shoulders and the cuts in his hands become, at times, sensations that fill the whole world of the story – just as they fill out unbearably the entire experience and awareness of the one man whose story it is. At such times, physical pain, narration, and meaning all flash together and become one thing, one event: this being the mark of that intensity already suggested to be the proof of the book's quality, as of its realism.

There is another reason why Hemingway emphasises touch; he uses it skilfully in the episode where Santiago first hooks the marlin. Notice how it marks the ironically gentle and intimate beginning of that firm bond of touch between man and fish that is broken only by the destruction of one and the return to shore of the other:

> He reached out for the line and held it softly between the thumb and forefinger of his right hand . . . Then it came again. This time it was a tentative pull, not solid nor heavy, and he knew exactly what it was. One hundred fathoms down a marlin was eating the sardines that covered the point and the shank of the hook . . . The old man held the line delicately, and softly . . . He felt the light delicate pulling and then a harder pull when a sardine's head must have been more difficult to break from the hook . . . 'Come on,' the old man said aloud. '. . . Don't be shy, fish. Eat them.'
>
> . . . He was happy feeling the gentle pulling and then he felt something hard and unbelievably heavy. It was the weight of the fish and he let the line slip down . . . As it went down, slipping lightly through the old man's fingers, he still could feel the great weight, though the pressure of his thumb and finger were almost imperceptible. (pp.38–40)

For Santiago, and therefore the reader, touch is a way of communicating. There is a powerful effect in the way the thumb and forefinger can communicate directly with the movements and with the bulk of a great fish swimming in the darkness six hundred feet down. We share in it: we feel the amazing tense link between two whole worlds, the human world of sea-surface and light, the fish-world of blackness and cold. Everything becomes intent and focussed: a man holding a thin line between two fingers and reading, like a surgeon, the meaning of every distant tremor. The life and strength of a fifteen-hundred-pound fish can be held delicately and dangerously between two fingers, as though it were an egg. The old man, communicating with the marlin by his touch, tries to communicate with it by speaking aloud – trying to send his thoughts along that gently vibrating cord of rope: 'Don't be shy, fish. Eat them.' He speaks humorously, almost like a father coaxing a child to eat. And his touch on the rope is as kindly and encouraging as if it were a spoon to feed a child. And what comes out of this? Not tenderness, but agony: agony for both man and fish; a 'touch' of agony and fire in the man's hands and back, in the fish's mouth and then the heart, that lasts for two days. And is not the whole story, from one point of view, about this kind of 'touch'? The communication that is a bond between hunter and hunted? The strange connection between tenderness and pain? Between man and nature? Burden, friction, pressure; desire; togetherness; then loneliness – do these things not come to our mind in *The Old Man and the Sea* through our participation in physical effects like these, rather than through our conscious perception of large ideas and themes? Perhaps ideas and values in life are always at their most true when they are rooted in physicality and in feeling.

You will find it useful to work this out a little more for yourself. Try studying the *variety* of kinds of 'touch' which the narrative employs. Then analyse the effect of the appeal to our sense of touch in the battle with the sharks. What does the emphasis on this particular kind of sensation tell us about the kind of man Santiago is?

Try looking at the whole episode from which quotation has been made, and see how many instances of *irony* you find in the bond of touch between Santiago and the marlin. And study, in this light of *irony*, the final harpooning of the fish:

> He felt the iron go in and he leaned on it and drove it further and then pushed all his weight after it . . . I think I felt his heart, he thought. When I pushed on the harpoon shaft the second time. (pp.93–5)

Facts

So far, it has been suggested that *The Old Man and the Sea* is to be seen *in the first place* not as a parable full of universal significance but as an exceptionally vivid re-creation of a series of events, which are given reality for us as we read by Hemingway's careful use of sensuous description. There *are* universal meanings that emerge from the story. But they must be seen to emerge, to come out of the experienced action of the plot, and not to be imposed by the author or solemnly extracted by the critic. It is in the very sense of emerging, of significance slowly and even painfully struggling to be born *through* events and facts, that the real value of the story lies.

The Old Man and the Sea is full of facts: surprising and precise facts that appeal to our sense of wonder and our instinctive love of practical knowledge. The power of the fiction depends on the skill with which these facts are used. They are not offered for their own sake: the book is hardly intended as a manual for us to study on how to catch marlin, or how to survive in an open boat. By appealing to our love of practical knowledge, Hemingway implicates our imagination in what is happening. That is, the facts are fundamentally a device, a technique of reassuring our sense of everyday values. They persuade us unconsciously to accept more readily everything that is less 'normal' in the story: everything that Hemingway has invented, and made more dramatic than in everyday life. Therefore the many facts about fishing and about the sea have a double function: they satisfy our sense of the real world, and they persuade us to accept the illusion of the fictional world. And this is what underlies Hemingway's famous statement, that his intention was always to convey to the reader 'the way it was'.

The precise but selective facts we are given about Santiago's way of life serve to focus very clearly our attitude to him as a man. A whole way of life is compressed into these simple facts about his home: that he lives in a shack made of palm-leaves, where there is one bed, one table, and one chair; two religious pictures on the walls; and one shelf on which lies his one clean shirt. And this is how he goes to bed:

> the old man took off his trousers and went to bed in the dark. He rolled his trousers up to make a pillow, putting the newspaper inside them. He rolled himself in the blanket and slept on the other old newspapers that covered the springs of the bed. (p.21)

Such facts as these could be used in different ways by different authors. We can imagine some novelist using them so as to create compassion for the sufferings of the poor, or anger at a social system that allowed such poverty. Another writer might use them comically, making the old man into a Charlie Chaplin figure: a clown arranging his newspapers with exaggerated care. Or a writer like Samuel Beckett might turn the facts of the old man going to bed into a symbol of the futility of life. But how does Hemingway use them? Not at all symbolically, but simply to convey to us the stripped-down and basic quality of Santiago's life. There is very little that stands between Santiago and the essential rhythms of life and death: only a newspaper, or a palm leaf, or a chair. His life is bare, stark, and close to nature. And thereby his life is prepared for a direct encounter with the natural violence and truth of the marlin.

We are aware of something else in the way the author portrays these few facts. We not only see that they tell us something about the quality of Santiago's life. We also recognise that the act of narration is itself stark and 'natural' in the case of Hemingway. By making us look at a few details very closely and unemotionally, without any 'trimmings' of style or commentary, Hemingway is trying to persuade us that the story, like the character, is close to nature. Our suspicions are allayed, and the implied 'voice' of the narrator, unemotional, crisp, aware of the realities of life, becomes one that we can trust. In fact, it is a voice that becomes almost our own as we read. And so, by this guarantee, we enter more fully into the story. It is worth asking yourself, at this point, what particular effect Hemingway gains by describing Santiago's dream of Africa immediately after the description of his going to bed. What contrasts does he set up of *facts* and of *style* between the two passages?

The factual description of Santiago's hut and how he goes to bed come early in the story, at a point where we are more aware of the presence of a presiding narrator than we are later on. Once the action has moved to sea, the perception of facts and events comes to us not from outside – not from a Hemingway watching and recording them – but from inside Santiago's own consciousness. In this way, the material facts that are recorded are simultaneously *internal* facts: events of thought and sensation inside Santiago's mind. What *he* sees and thinks and feels becomes (with some exceptions) the whole world of the book, and the way *he* measures and remembers and plans becomes the boundaries of the whole narrative action. The *fact* – an interesting fact in itself – that there is one precise unmarked spot on a shark's head where the brain can be pierced does not stand out of the narrative, like a fact for us to jot down and use again. It is a fact in *his* consciousness at a particular time, and it is a fact, therefore, that is emmeshed in feeling, colour, movement, and everything else that makes up the drama of our reading experience at that point. The fact cannot be separated from its context. (And perhaps no fact, anywhere in life, can be fully detached from the context of the man who sees it, or the place where it happens, and so on?)

It might be helpful at this stage to compare, very briefly, the way Hemingway uses facts about the sea and fishing with the method of Herman Melville (1819–91) in *Moby Dick* (1851) – that other great American classic about a sea-hunt. Melville's novel, like Hemingway's story, is packed with information. It is a veritable Bible of whaling lore: a treatise, a travelogue, and a catalogue. Melville often alternates between the method of the documentary and the method of the poetic meditation. And this is a polarity – an exciting but problematic polarity – that Hemingway avoids. Take as an example how each approaches the part played by the rope: the line attached to the harpoon in whaling as in marlin-fishing. Melville devotes a whole chapter to describing what the rope is made of (it is Chapter 60, 'The Line'), its thickness, its strength, how it is stowed away, fastened, joined to other lines; how it uncoils dangerously, sometimes plucking men out of the boat; and so on, in intricate and fascinating detail. Then it ends this way:

> But why say more? All men live enveloped in whale-lines. All are born with halters round their necks; but it is only when caught in the swift, sudden turn of death, that mortals realise the silent, subtle, ever-present perils of life.*

That is, Melville very typically *amasses* his facts at great length; then suddenly makes his heap of facts glow with allegorical meaning. The movement is always from his detailed observation of the world towards his own mind: not the mind of any character in the novel, but the mind of the narrator himself, which interprets and absorbs that world into itself.

Contrast Melville's use of facts with Hemingway's. We learn a lot about Santiago's fishing-lines, almost as much as we do about Melville's. But the facts come to us within a context of action and of consciousness, not listed for us by an author:

> In the darkness he loosened his sheath knife and taking all the strain of the fish on his left shoulder he leaned back and cut the line against the wood of the gunwhale. Then he cut the other line closest to him and in the dark made the loose ends of the reserve coils fast. He worked skilfully with the one hand and put his foot on the coils to hold them as he drew his knots tight. Now he had six reserve coils of line. There were two from each bait he had severed and the two from the bait the fish had taken and they were all connected.

*Herman Melville, *Moby Dick*, Penguin Books, Harmondsworth, 1972, p.387.

> After it is light, he thought, I will work back to the forty-fathom bait and cut it away too and link up the reserve coils. I will have lost two hundred fathoms of good Catalan *cordel* and the hooks and leaders. That can be replaced. But who replaces this fish if I hook some fish and it cuts him off? (pp.48–9)

Hemingway does not allegorise his facts in this instance; nor does he give them to us directly *as* facts. They come to us, rather, as *experience*. We know the rope by the feel of it, not the measurement. And when we are given measurements and facts – six reserve coils, forty fathoms of bait-line, two hundred fathoms of Catalan *cordel*, the hooks and leaders – the facts do not end in themselves but are part of a whole surrounding scheme of action, purpose, time, and feeling. The facts, that is, are illuminated by hope, by determination, by regret, and by pain. And in this way they are given a different kind of imaginative life from the life that Melville's very different method provides. Hemingway's method is dramatic; Melville's, in this instance of it, is meditative.

Action and drama

Drama is partly a matter of rhythm: pulsation and movement. And this story is full of very distinct rhythms, based on alternations of varying kinds. There is a continual alternation between recollection and present action. Between sudden bursts of activity and crisis, Santiago reflects on the past or on the meaning of the present. Much of the story consists of the brooding and thinking that fill the long periods of agonised waiting. And within those periods of thought and preparation we are aware of suspense: what will the next sudden event be? When will the marlin surface? and so on. That is, the reflective pause contains tense anticipations of the next action, and the action, after bursting upon us, is then re-absorbed into Santiago's consciousness and into *our* meditative evaluation. Event, thought; thought, event. A man striking; then a man, locked passively in the great tension of the rope, thinking, sleeping a little, regretting, resolving . . . This is one of the basic rhythms of life, and it gives *The Old Man and the Sea* its unforgettably exciting and recognisable tempo. Here is one of the most effective of these moments of dramatic rhythm:

> After that he began to dream of the long yellow beach and he saw the first of the lions come down onto it in the early dark and then the other lions came and he rested his chin on the wood of the bows where the ship lay anchored with the evening off-shore breeze and he waited to see if there would be more lions and he was happy.

> The moon had been up for a long time but he slept on and the fish pulled on steadily and the boat moved into the tunnel of clouds.
>
> He woke with the jerk of his right fist coming up against his face and the line burning out through his right hand. He had no feeling of his left hand but he braked all he could with his right and the line rushed out . . . (pp.80–1)

There are at least three different components, three kinds of contrasted movement in this passage. Try to analyse how each leads into the other and produces the 'rhythm' and excitement described above.

Some other alternations that give the story its living pulse and energy are these: the alternation between the recurrent thought of land and a present awareness of the sea; and between the placid surface of the sea and what happens in its depths (both of these contrasts are again very typical of *Moby Dick*). There is the sense of the journey outwards, set against the return to shore; night against day, cold against heat, relaxation and exhaustion against sudden challenge and physical deed. One of the best-known critics of Hemingway, Carlos Baker, has attractively described this rhythm as being like that of the sea itself; though it might equally be seen as a rhythm characteristic of all literature of an epic or heroic kind, and one found particularly in folk-tale and ballad.

Some readers may find it interesting to search for this kind of effect – the alternation of tension with relaxation – in the tales of adventure and hunting in their own national tradition. Is Hemingway's use of rhythm more artful, more thought-out, than that of a folk-tale? Can you think of any national tale that you can compare with *The Old Man and the Sea* so as to bring out the respective merits of each as a narrative?

Another example of a dramatic rhythm-through-contrast can be found in Hemingway's ability, in the midst of sudden movement and action, to 'freeze' a scene, and create a moment of *static picture*. He does so as a literary device, of course: a way of flashing what he judges to be most significant on to the mind's inner eye, and etching it there unforgettably. But it is a device that is based upon a natural fact of experience. The mind does often work in this way, remembering only one vivid gesture, or one moment in an event when persons or things are related in a particular way: an outstretched arm, an angle of the head, a strange grouping of contrasted or similar figures. With experience flowing past us confusedly, the mind often has to seize a shape, or impose a shape, and so hold for our memory what would otherwise be blurred and lost. The mind is at times a camera; and the narrator, particularly the narrator of short stories, uses this fact to great effect. It is one of the things that drama does, too. It arranges an event, outlines it clearly, and imprints a scene, like an image, on our minds.

Here is a small example of Hemingway, like a camera, imposing stillness on an event, focussing intently on Santiago sitting asleep in his shack, and providing us with an unmoving and permanent picture:

> They were strange shoulders, still powerful although very old, and the neck was still strong too and the creases did not show so much when the old man was asleep and his head fallen forward. His shirt had been patched so many times that it was like the sail and the patches were faded to many different shades by the sun. The old man's head was very old though and with his eyes closed there was no life in his face. The newspaper lay across his knees and the weight of his arm held it there in the evening breeze. He was barefooted. (pp.14–15)

Such quiet concentration of observation is not merely a vivid piece of recording, a click of the camera. It also contrasts with the talk and the movement that have gone on before, and the action that will soon galvanise the old man's tired body. And in this way it adds to the variety and the intensity of the narrative's vitality. It is both pictorial *and* part of a drama.

Underlying much of the varying activity of the story, while Santiago is at sea, is the one static picture of the old man, with the rope around his shoulders, leaning against the bow of the skiff, being towed – eternally, it seems. That is, a glimpsed picture of something still and unchanging, set amidst so much that is flurried and unexpected: as though there are two planes of reality, and two kinds of time-scheme, superimposed on one another. It is like the moment of the great marlin's death, when the fish leaps for the last time, and just for a moment seems to have leapt *out* of time: 'He seemed to hang in the air above the old man in the skiff'. And after the last crash of spray and the death-throes, the fish's movement, like its life, dies into a perfectly held and composed picture. It is in itself a vignette of dramatic contrasts, in which the shapeless vividness of colour, the vague cloud-like spreading of the blood, and the immensity of depth are offset by the close presence of the fish as a mere silver object and by the harsh angular line of the projecting harpoon:

> he saw the fish was on his back with his silver belly up. The shaft of the harpoon was projecting at an angle from the fish's shoulder and the sea was discolouring with the red of the blood from his heart. First it was dark as a shoal in the blue water that was more than a mile deep. Then it spread like a cloud. The fish was silvery and still and floated with the waves. (p.94)

These are the great moments of Hemingway's art in *The Old Man and the Sea*: where the perfect interplay of flow and stillness, finality and continuation, act like a dramatic poem, and the story shapes itself, without allegory and without ostentatious comment, towards an eternal statement.

Character

The dramatic quality of the story is created partly by the way the events come to us through the consciouness not of the narrator but of the central character. And this raises the issue of whether and how 'character' matters in *The Old Man and the Sea.* Obviously there is an old man, called Santiago, with specific characteristics. But is the story primarily a study of his mind and temperament, or is it something else? As readers, do we focus primarily on who the old man is, or on what he does, or on the meaning of what he does? It may in the end not be possible to detach fully any one of these alternatives from the others, but the questions are worth asking – and they are worth asking before we are tempted into trying to compile any ambitious 'character-sketch' of Santiago. There are some accounts of this story that labour over the few details of Santiago's nature – and even over Manolin's – as though Hemingway's subject-matter was a complex human psyche rather than a fishing-story.

What do we learn of Santiago? He is old and poor, but spiritually undefeated. He reminisces and has his dreams, like most old men; is simple, patient, dignified, and humble; and, being knowledgeable about his craft, is still full of 'tricks'. Physically, he is surprisingly powerful. He has feelings of tenderness and pity – for example, for the boy, for birds, for turtles, and for the fish he catches. He respects the sea, and the things of the sea – though he dislikes 'false' things, like the Portuguese man-of-war. That is, he is a man who is both active and contemplative. He can endure suffering and employ his mind and his hands with practical efficiency; and from time to time he is able to stand outside his practical life and see it in larger terms. Both of these aspects of Santiago's mind can be seen in the following extract, where his thought focusses first on the practical usefulness of having the boy's help, then moves to an imaginative identification with the marlin, then to a sense of 'the world' and its fate, before moving back to a sense of himself, and finally to a practical reminder about eating in order to survive:

> 'I wish the boy was here,' he said aloud and settled himself against the rounded planks of the bow and felt the strength of the great fish

> through the line he held across his shoulders moving steadily toward whatever he had chosen.
>
> When once, through my treachery, it had been necessary to him to make a choice, the old man thought.
>
> His choice had been to stay in the deep dark water far out beyond all snares and traps and treacheries. My choice was to go there to find him beyond all people. Beyond all people in the world. Now we are joined together and have been since noon. And no one to help either of us.
>
> Perhaps I should not have been a fisherman, he thought. But that was the thing I was born for. I must surely remember to eat the tuna after it gets light. (p.48)

You will find it useful to make an analysis of some other passages that demonstrate the combination of practicality and reflection in Santiago's thinking. And you could ask yourself two questions about him:

> How limited in scope is his reflective faculty?
>
> Does he 'develop' as a thinker in the progress of the story?

There are other things to say about Santiago. For example, he shows a kind of pride that is almost theatrical at times, and that we might identify as being characteristically 'Spanish' (in his case, of course, Latin-American). Equally, we might identify it as being characteristically 'heroic' in a literary and epic way:

> He spat into the ocean and said, 'Eat that, *Galanos*. And make a dream you've killed a man.' (p.120)

Similarly, we could point out that he seems to be religious to a certain degree, though at times he wishes to deny it. He says prayers, but only when he has to, or thinks it might be a way of placating some natural force that opposes him. He believes in luck more easily than in God or in a Church, and his religiousness seems essentially primitive and 'instinctual'. But this is to anticipate what remains to be said, at the end, about the overall purport or meaning of the story: a meaning that emerges only after we have immersed ourselves as readers and as critics in the story's texture – its action, its language, its sense of character.

Santiago offers very little in the way of 'depth' or 'development' as a character. He is made sufficiently individual, but there is a great deal of the 'type' about him. He is something of a national type – the self-dramatising and tragically-aware Latin male. He is something of a literary type – the bold folk-hero slaying a sea-monster (though the marlin seems relatively harmless), and revealing the sufferings of life and the virtues of stoicism and endurance. And he is something of a human type – the old peasant who has seen much, is closer to nature than other people (like the tourists at the end), and evokes some compassion, admiration, and a little humour in those who surround him.

The boy Manolin, too, is a type, not an individual. He is the Faithful Apprentice, who tends the old man, studies his ways, and embodies hope for the future. He is used successfully by Hemingway in this story; the point is that he is *used*. That is, the boy conveys little sense of having an existence outside the story. He is a function of the story, and a device to carry out the story's intentions. 'Character' in fiction usually presents two aspects: that of having 'life' and that of having a 'function'. The emphasis varies from work to work, but there is almost always a mixture of both aspects. In some works, the sense of a character 'living' outside the boundaries of the story is very strong. The most famous example of this might be the character of Shakespeare's Hamlet; but one could also suggest examples such as Mark Twain's (1835–1910) Huckleberry Finn or many of Leo Tolstoy's (1828–1910) characters. In other works, the characters are more obviously part of the structure and argument. They may appear as symbols, or as caricatures, or – as in this case of *The Old Man and the Sea* – as broad, recognisable types of humanity. Fictional characters that tend more towards 'function' than towards individual 'life' should not be seen as necessarily inferior for that reason, but simply as belonging to a somewhat different mode of art. And when we call Santiago and Manolin 'types' we are not criticising Hemingway's art, only trying to identify the kind of art it is.

It will be helpful to think a little more about this question of 'characters' and 'types'. Are there certain points in the story where we are more aware than at other points of Santiago as a 'personality', distinct from the author and from the ideas the author may wish to embody in him?

Once you have thought of Santiago as a 'type', you could make out a list of the things about him that are *not* typical and general, but particular and unique.

What 'characters' can you think of in other books you have read that are *more* symbolical, *more* functional and two-dimensional than Santiago?

Feeling

Hemingway's use of sensory perceptions and facts; the action of his story coming to the reader in terms of dramatic contrasts and rhythms; the way in which 'character' is part of the texture of the whole fiction, all these things are part of the *flesh* of the story, part of how it affects the reader who submits his mind to it as he reads. There are two other vital elements of the story at this primary level of the way we actually experience it. The first of these is *feeling*; and the second is *language*.

What variety and what quality of feeling do we find within the reading experience we call *The Old Man and the Sea*? We find pity, admiration, a great deal of half-fearful anticipation, a shared physical pain, some gentleness and affection, a touch of nostalgia, a little anger and contempt, profound disappointment and resentment, and in the end that strange qualified happiness that comes, after suffering, from a renewed confidence in the self. Perhaps all of these feelings centre around and are controlled by the dominant experience of *being tested*. We share in the sense of certain human powers being stretched to the point of breaking. We fear for ourselves, as we read. We share in moments of relief: the memories of the past, the thought of the boy Manolin, the escape into the golden dream of Africa, the kindness of Manolin at the beginning and at the end, the occasional flashes of sardonic humour from Santiago himself, the continual pleasure we take in the beauty and colour of the sea. But fundamentally our feeling is one of threat, test, and recovery. In identifying ourselves temporarily with the experiences of Santiago, qualified by other experiences outside his consciousness created for us by the author's own perceptions and his art, we come quite close to an imagined experience of disintegration. We are made to know what it is to come to the brink of letting go, of seeing a great achievement reduced to nothingness, of being broken in the body and almost in the spirit. And running alongside this feeling – which is something of a nightmare feeling of loss and death – there is the counter-feeling of re-integration. Santiago's closeness – and therefore *our* closeness – to the fish, and to the life and selfhood of the fish, is a *constructive* experience. So, too, is the sense that we will not break, and that we are moving towards the experience of a new *knowledge*: knowledge about man and beast, the individual and nature, that knowledge about our place in the universe which we call our sense of destiny. So, as readers, we achieve peace, and are in the end confirmed in our sense of ourselves.

These are very difficult things to put into words – and no reader should accept blindly the words of any critic or teacher. You should consider whether there is any truth for *you* in the suggestion that in reading *The Old Man and the Sea* we feel – in emotion, in imagination – a little of what it is and what it means to come towards death and to turn back again towards life.

There is one question for critical judgement that always comes up in discussions of Hemingway, and is particularly appropriate when *feeling* is the point at issue. Does Hemingway relapse into sentimentality at any point? If a writer approaches his material with an emotional response that is crude or brutal, say, or immature, or artificial, or over-simple, then his work suffers in quality. In some of his other works Hemingway could quite fairly be criticised for invoking an emotional response of, say, admiration or pity that is too facile, too glib. At times, we feel that life is more complex, and human feeling more complex, than the emotion Hemingway allows for. Examples might be the feeling of contempt we are clearly expected to share for Robert Cohn in *The Sun Also Rises*, or of hero-worship for Cantwell in *Across the River and into the Trees*, or the complacent self-pity that underlies the whole presentation of Harry Morgan in *To Have and Have Not*.

What are the danger-areas in *The Old Man and the Sea*? One dangerous area might have been the portrayal of Manolin. The boy might have so easily been used as a device simply for bringing tears to our eyes in his caring for Santiago. Hemingway handles the tenderness of the relationship discreetly and well. In a treatment that was sentimental, the feeling of tenderness would be allowed to swamp the facts of the situation. But the formality of the language between the boy and the old man acts as a controlling form: their relationship, while based on feeling, also relies on a certain distance being maintained between them. Their conversation is not intimate but restrained, detached, and even slightly ritualistic:

> 'Lie down, old man, and I will bring you your clean shirt. And something to eat.'
>
> 'Bring any of the papers of the time that I was gone', the old man said.
>
> 'You must get well fast for there is much that I can learn and you can teach me everything. How much did you suffer?'
>
> 'Plenty', the old man said.
>
> 'I'll bring the food and the papers', the boy said (p.126)

The possible sentimentality and emotional excess in their relationship is prevented by this formality, and by the very quality of their being 'types' which we have already observed.

Similarly, the recurrent references to Santiago's dream of Africa, where lions play on the beach, could have been over-soft and embarrassing. But they appear economically, and are not dwelt upon or over-stressed by an author anxious to move us with a vision of lost youth and lost innocence. By their succinctness they appear as convincing dream-images; and the reality of wakeful life breaks into them quickly, controlling and *guiding* the feeling that these images create.

Again, there are very few instances in the description of Santiago's sufferings and heroism that might make us suspect Hemingway of wringing too much emotion out of the events ('sentimentality' often suggests the picture of someone squeezing water out of a cloth). The old man says oracular things, but not at great length. And the solemnity of some of his pronouncements is quickly qualified by his recognition of practical necessities. That is, the heroic note of what he says and of how Hemingway regards him is reduced by coming up against commonplace thoughts and things. For example:

> 'But man is not made for defeat', he said. 'A man can be destroyed but not defeated'. I am sorry that I killed the fish though, he thought. Now the bad time is coming and I do not even have the harpoon. (p.103)

Santiago's opening statement there is very literary and rhetorical, and perhaps a little worryingly unrealistic on the lips of a poor fisherman. If Hemingway had allowed Santiago to go on in this vein the *feeling* of the passage would quickly have become strained and artificial: too melodramatic and bombastic. But the passage is saved by his sudden regret for the fish and for the lost harpoon. The regret brings the feeling down to earth, keeps it human and natural. In sentimentality – and false heroics can be as much part of sentimentality as tearfulness over a child – the feeling escapes from its context, and is cultivated for its own sake. Feeling that has 'quality' in literature is connected with all the complex realities of the human situation that surrounds it: it is braced and qualified by little ironies, changes of tone, respect for everyday realities, and by an author's unfaltering grasp of the human *details* of an event or scene. And in this story, though certainly not in all his stories or novels, Hemingway has a saving sense of variation of tone, concision of expression, and an eye for facts. No great literature exists without strong feeling; but strong feeling can be a dangerous marlin, and can tow an author out to sea.

At this point you might ask yourself whether there are any places in *The Old Man and the Sea* where you find Hemingway less successful than has been claimed above in preserving a mature control over emotion?

Is there any justification in the contradictory charge that Hemingway does not show *enough* feeling in the story?

Try to think of an example of 'sentimentality' in any other literary work you know, and compare specific examples of it with scenes from this story.

Language

Hemingway is famous for his language: perhaps too famous. With much care and effort, he created a very influential and immediately recognisable style that is almost *too* influential on himself. It became an end in itself for him, rather than an instrument to be adapted and varied according to the different demands made by different subject-matter. The style he created in his early work, such as *In Our Time* and *The Sun Also Rises*, was almost too good. Like the style of certain painters, it tended to become a *manner*, rather than a flexible way of responding to experience and conveying fresh insights through words. Its nature and its qualities are easy to grasp. It avoids complicated syntax, and where it does not use a simple, short sentence it connects the various parts of the sentence in a straightforward, sequential way, often linked by 'and'. It uses adjectives and abstract nouns sparingly. The simple sentences and the repeated rhythms take on a biblical note, and hint at the profundities that the 'surface' of the language tries to ignore. It draws attention to itself, as though to say to the reader, 'Life is so complicated, and probably so disastrous, that I am picking my way with nervous precision, like a man who has once been injured learning to walk again with tension and care'. It focusses with intensity on specific details, in the ways we have already seen. And underlying this closeness of focus is the implied statement, 'I will *not* be distracted from this one true thing I have got hold of, because if I allow myself to be distracted into qualifications and subtleties I will lose trace of it, and the darkness of chaos will flood in'. This nervousness gives the style its excitement. But it certainly prevents it from being the simple and completely unsubjective recording of events that it usually pretends to be. It is artificial, often in the best sense: in the sense that poetry is artificial. But at times it dangerously contradicts itself, in that it tells us to look with a new directness and clarity at life and yet imposes itself as a distinct lens or filter between us and what we observe. It may well be that this is a contradiction inherent in the nature of art.

Here is an example, chosen almost at random, of the language of *The Old Man and the Sea* at its simplest, flattest, and least mannered:

> He rested for what he believed to be two hours. The moon did not rise now until late and he had no way of judging the time. Nor was he really resting except comparatively. He was still bearing the pull of the fish across his shoulders but he placed his left hand on the gunwale of the bow and confided more and more of the resistance to the fish to the skiff itself. (p.75)

Even the awkwardness of that last phrase, 'the resistance to the fish to the skiff itself', seems to be a guarantee of honesty and accuracy. In trying to get at exactly what is happening, the language seems to imply, it does not matter if something inelegant occurs.

Occasionally, but only occasionally, Hemingway allows himself a very literary turn of phrase, usually in the form of a simile: 'The sail was patched with flour sacks and, furled, it looked like the flag of permanent defeat' (p.5). Or again, also at the beginning of the story: 'none of these scars were fresh. They were as old as erosions in a fishless desert' (p.6). Such figures of speech, drawing attention to the author's intention, are unusual, and perhaps not wholly successful.

Again, at specific moments, the style takes on a colour and a sonority that are meant to stand out by contrast, and to convey the sense of an important turning-point or climax:

> He took all his pain and what was left of his long gone pride and he put it against the fish's agony and the fish came over on to his side and swam gently on his side, his bill almost touching the planking of the skiff, and started to pass the boat, long, deep, wide, silver and barred with purple and interminable in the water. (p.93)

No one could say that the language in that one-sentence paragraph was commonplace or natural. The sentence builds up its parts in a carefully laborious sequence – 'all his pain and what was left of his strength and his long gone pride' – that emulates the movement of the exhausted marlin and the physical strain of the fisherman. It makes deliberate and uncolloquial use of emotive abstractions: 'strength' and 'pride' are pitted against 'the fish's agony'. And it mounts to a heavy crescendo in the very un-prosaic inversion of adjectives – 'long, deep, wide' – ending in the virtually poetic cadence, 'interminable in the water'.

The dialogue, too, is a blend of the realistic and the artificial: usually realistic in content yet stylised in expression. Hemingway's dialogue in his other writing is often stylised in various ways. But in this story it has the very peculiar kind of stylisation gained from the pretence that it is an English version of the Spanish that Santiago and Manolin would speak in real life. Since we are meant to realise that Santiago could not possibly speak like this, since English is not his tongue anyway, we are more likely to accept other artificialities of the dialogue. Using the device of a pretended 'translation', which would be bound to be stilted in any case, Hemingway can 'poetise' the dialogue as he wishes (aided, as we have seen before, by our acceptance of the national stereotype of the self-dramatising, large-gestured Latin). The speakers are 'distanced' from us to a certain degree, and the language, while taking on a kind of epic dignity, does not lose its convincingness. Even slightly strange exchanges like the following become fairly acceptable, once we grow used to the convention that the dialogue comes to us at a remove – like seeing people move on the other side of a coloured glass:

> 'You're my alarm clock', the boy said.
> 'Age is my alarm clock', the old man said. 'Why do old men wake so early? Is it to have one longer day?'
> 'I don't know', the boy said. 'All I know is that young boys sleep late and hard'.
> 'I can remember it', the old man said. 'I'll waken you in time'. (p.20)

At times, the effect is faintly comic, perhaps unintentionally. At other times, the comedy is surely deliberate, as in the conversation between Santiago and Manolin about American baseball, where the epic tone gained by the pretended 'translation' is more suitable for a conversation between Homer's Agamemnon and Achilles, say, about the prospects for the next day's battle before the walls of Troy:

> 'The Yankees cannot lose'.
> 'But I fear the Indians of Cleveland'.
> 'Have faith in the Yankees my son. Think of the great DiMaggio'.
> 'I fear both the Tigers of Detroit and the Indians of Cleveland'.
> 'Be careful or you will fear even the Reds of Cincinnati and the White Sox of Chicago'. (p.13)

It would have been difficult for Hemingway to sustain this epic, or mock-epic, tone through much conversation between people. But most of the 'speech' in the story comes from Santiago talking to himself at sea, and becomes an acceptable, if highly formalised, element of the whole. He continues to speak like an oracle. But it may be that oracles invite less ridicule when talking to themselves than to an audience.

Hemingway's language of narrative and dialogue, then, like his characterisation, combines elements that are 'realistic' with elements that are 'stylised' and 'heightened'. The effect of this latter quality in a work of literature can only be to increase the tendency of the work to utter a 'statement' about life. *The Old Man and the Sea* is a dramatic narrative, a piece of imagined action, rather than an essay; and the reader should learn to analyse and respond to its qualities as a narrative rather than to extract its 'meaning'. The reader arrives at the meaning of a story in the way one comes to 'know' a friend: in little flashes of sudden insight and connection that occur inside the ordinary, day-to-day processes of living together. We 'read' our friends dramatically, from *within* a total relationship, not like public notices or scientific statements, from the outside.

The fable

When Hemingway said of this story, 'I tried to make a real old man, a real boy, a real sea and a real fish and real sharks', he then went on to say, 'But if I made them good and true enough they would mean many things' (*Time*, 13 December, 1954). The 'many things' are perhaps not as many as the amount and variety of published interpretations of this story would suggest. Some have seen it as a symbolic account of the confrontation between Man and the Absolute, in which the marlin represents the Universe. Others have taken its occasional hints of Christian significance to mean it is a Christian allegory, with Santiago as Christ (the rope-burns in his hands equalling the stigmata, and the cramp in his left hand being a reference to the malefactor on Christ's left hand at the Crucifixion!). And more than a few critics have read it as a conscious allegory of Hemingway's own career as an artist, in which the pursuit of the marlin equals his pursuit of artistic perfection, and the sharks equal his unsympathetic critics. It is possible to see *why* people have over-interpreted the story in these and other ways: there is at least a tiny scrap of truth in most such interpretations. But to read *The Old Man and the Sea* as an allegory is to impose significance, not to uncover it. And it means doing violence to the way the narrative actually works upon our minds as we read. Hemingway's view of life is often revealed only too explicitly in his other works. It is a view of life of such limitations that it suffers cruelly if exposed in the form of allegory or open argument, as it is, for example, in Frederic Henry's famous parable of the ants in the last chapter of *A Farewell to Arms*. When the philosophy is itself restricted by, and limited to, the material offered by the narrative action itself, its meaning becomes the more plausible, and even—paradoxically—the more satisfyingly universal.

Insofar as *The Old Man and the Sea* tends towards, and just towards, the nature of the fable—that is, a compressed action conveying some general human significance—its purport seems to be along the following lines. Beneath all the complexities and the trappings of our civilised life—the trappings beneath which people like the tourists on the last page of the story cannot see—there remain certain stark and primitive realities. These are the realities that we have to go back to folk-tales and to the epics of antiquity to see again with clarity: hence certain deliberate stylistic features in the writing of this story. We live by companionship and love—such as Santiago's for the boy, and the boy's for Santiago. We live by remembering our own youth, and the strengths of our early manhood—as in Santiago's dream, and his memory of the hand-wrestling with the negro which establishes his reputation for strength. But we must also live in loneliness, seeking out our private destiny in confronting the implacable and unknowable power of the things we cannot control in the world about us. Santiago does this in order to live. His battle with the marlin is not that of the sportsman, but of the man who is himself part of nature and must live off some other living thing. He belongs to the enormous economy of the natural world—as we all do in the end, conceal it by our man-made economies as we try to do.

Santiago is not like Captain Ahab in Melville's novel *Moby Dick*, directly seeking out knowledge about the universe, or trying to *conquer* nature. He is not the damned Romantic hero, but simply—what comes closer to most of us—man-struggling-to-live. In this struggle, he learns to understand and respect his adversary. He even knows love for the marlin. That is, there is a kind of companionship revealed by the contest of wills between the man and the fish. The story does not suggest that man is alone in a hostile universe, but that he belongs to and within a natural process. His life is not meaningless, but plays a part in a larger system of meaning—even though (it is implied by Santiago's reliance on 'luck') we can never understand that system by any of our normal logical ways of thought, or even by the ways of conventional religion. The story seems to confirm that certain human responses, like pity (for example, for the turtles), anger (against the sharks), determination, practical application, and self-questioning, are not delusive but real, and that they are sustained, rather than undermined, by nature. Luck and endurance seem to be equally important. The need to have luck signifies that the world is at least in part ruled by Chance rather than by anything that resembles the human mind. But the need to have endurance signifies that it seems to be worthwhile surviving, and that to develop the self is not just a sterile exercise in narcissism—a man flexing his muscles in front of a mirror, in an empty universe—but a fulfilling of what the universe expects and teaches.

Half-comically, the recurrent image of Joe DiMaggio, the baseball hero painfully handicapped in his career by a heel-injury, becomes the fisherman's patron saint of endurance. Santiago's unreliable left hand is the equivalent of DiMaggio's 'bone-spur' in the heel: to be alive at all means being vulnerable, open to pain, and destined to die. Life will always find out a man's weakness—his mortality—in the end. But as life tests him, it forces him to develop certain virtues—and in this way, perhaps, the hostility and indifference of nature is morally 'justified'. At least, a testing such as Santiago undergoes confirms his sense of 'belonging' in the world. He recognises his own destiny in the destiny that confronts the bird, when it lands unexpectedly (and ironically) to rest on the very rope that is stretched taut between the man and the doomed fish. When he sees the bird Santiago thinks, grimly but resignedly, of the hawks that are waiting for it once it has rested sufficiently to fly on towards the land:

> 'Take a good rest, small bird', he said. 'Then go in and take your chance like any man or bird or fish.' (p.53)

The man or bird or fish who takes his chance in life—and the odds seem to be that the hawks will get him—will have to go his way alone. But the rope of agony that connects Santiago and the marlin suggests a strange but vital companionship. *The Old Man and the Sea* interweaves these two concepts of life: its essential loneliness and its unbreakable togetherness. Santiago, deprived of the boy who might have helped him, deprived for a while of the support of one of his own hands, is nevertheless supported throughout his ordeal by the thought of others. On shore, for all his 'strangeness', we see him as part of a community, looked after by Manolin, helped by Martin, the owner of the Terrace, and by Pedrico, at the *bodega*, always aware of other people like the skipper of Manolin's boat. He sits on the Terrace, enjoys credit at the coffee-shack. And the other fishermen, whether they laugh at him or are sympathetic, are very much aware of his presence. He remembers his social success in the past, when he became *El Campeón.* And his interest in the *gran ligas* of American baseball seems to take him out of himself and link him to a wider world. Above all, in his relationship to his craft and to the birds and myriad life of the sea, Santiago demonstrates that 'no man was ever alone on the sea'. There is a touching but quite unsentimental intimacy in his relationship to the terns, the warbler, the man-of-war bird, the turtles, the tuna, the flying fish, the porpoise ('They play and make jokes and love one another. They are our brothers like the flying fish').

The most vital relationship of all, of course, is the one that develops between Santiago and the marlin: between the hunter and the hunted. It is in many ways a physical relationship: Santiago bears the living weight of the marlin on his own body as he is towed through the sea. He feels, between his finger and thumb, the deep-down delicate nibbling of the marlin's mouth as it first takes the bait; then every lunge and tremor and slackening of the great fish's pull; till in the end he feels the marlin's heart as he pushes home the harpoon. He even eats a little of the flesh of the marlin that is his 'brother' as it floats alongside, tied to the boat and therefore tied to the man in the boat. And when the sharks rip at its flesh, it is the old man who suffers the pain of dismemberment. It is also a relationship of the imagination: a triumph of the *moral* imagination, which can identify with the life of another, and on which all moral values and moral action are based. From the very first, Santiago is able to identify with the marlin in all its moods, in its panic, its calm, its cunning, its dignity, its ebb and flow of the will. His habit of talking aloud to himself—perfectly natural in an old man, and not simply a useful device imposed by the narrator—fosters the sense of relationship, and articulates the growing recognition of brotherhood. The human and the non-human are indissolubly linked by the mutual process of living and dying, and of killing in order to live:

> You are killing me, fish, the old man thought. But you have a right to. Never have I seen a greater, or more beautiful, or a calmer or more noble thing than you, brother. Come on and kill me. I do not care who kills who. (p.92)

In imagining the great fish, hundreds of feet below him in the sea, Santiago's mind always turns to an image of himself, stressing how instinctive and natural it is to see oneself in others, and others in oneself:

> Now that he had seen him once, he could picture the fish swimming in the water with his purple pectoral fins set wide as wings and the great erect tail slicing through the dark. I wonder how much he sees at that depth, the old man thought. His eye is huge and a horse, with much less eye, can see in the dark. Once I could see quite well in the dark. Not in the absolute dark. But almost as a cat sees. (p.65)

And in the end, when the fish is dead, and being attacked and eaten by the sharks, Santiago's resistance becomes a resistance of two-in-one:

> 'Half-fish', he said. 'Fish that you were. I am sorry that I went too far out. I ruined us both. But we have killed many sharks, you and I, and ruined many others. How many did you ever kill, old fish? You do not have that spear on your head for nothing.'
>
> He liked to think of the fish and what he could do to a shark if he were swimming free. I should have chopped the bill off to fight them with, he thought. But there was no hatchet and then there was no knife.
>
> But if I had, and could have lashed it to an oar butt, what a weapon. Then we might have fought them together. What will you do now if they come in the night? What can you do?
>
> 'Fight them', he said. 'I'll fight them until I die'. (p.116)

The fusion of the two, man and fish, becomes complete as Santiago's apology—'I am sorry that I went too far out'—passes into the idea of the two of them joining in fighting the sharks. There is even a significant ambiguity of language at the end of the passage, for when Santiago, having talked of 'I' and 'we', then asks, 'What can you do?', the 'you' could mean either himself *or* the marlin *or* both of them as one.

So here we have a story that down to the very details of its language—as in its physical setting, and as in its occasional phrases of explicit philosophic utterance—emphasises that we are at the same time solitaries in an uncertain world *and* members of that world. The sharks and the Portuguese man-of-war have their part to play. And the solitary man, cheated by the natural world of what he won, and almost broken by it, is at the end planning his next fishing expedition with better weapons and new 'tricks'. Santiago, 'strange' as he is, remains a realist and a man of practicalities. His withdrawal into sleep and the dream of lions, in the last scene, is not a movement into death, or an acceptance of the finality of isolation. On the contrary, it is a moment's submersion in the deeper springs of the self in order that individuality and strength can be re-born; that the past can continue to be brought to life in the present; and that the perpetual tragic adventure of forging the self's relationships with an alluring but destructive world can begin again. The story does not end in any large revelation or in any clearly recommended code of conduct. There is no religious or philosophic vision. It ends, like the greatest fables, in certain memorable images: the skeleton of a great fish, waiting to return to the sea; the inadequacy of words to express truth, as when the waiter's ambiguous words mislead the tourists; and the image of old age joined to youth, and preparing for a fresh start. Another story is about to be written, and *we* are its plot.

Part 4

Hints for study

Some general points

There are two fundamental things to bear in mind when studying a text systematically, and with an examination (alas!) in mind. *Take notes continually as you read*; and *ask yourself questions at every point*. It is very difficult to force yourself to take notes on your own reading. Most readers resist it as a kind of mechanical imposition that destroys the naturalness of the act of reading, and interrupts the flow of narrative. But it is essential for any student to form the habit. Have some spare paper always folded into your edition of the book, and write down any point at all that comes into your mind as you read and seems reasonably relevant at the time. Don't worry if some of the things you jot down strike you later as wrong, or irrelevant. The essential thing is not to let slip any idea or impression that the text conveys to your mind at the time. As in fishing, so in studying: you are always exasperated later by the ideas—like the fish—that escaped, and will not be caught again. Don't trust the ability of the mind to seize and hold its perceptions: most minds are very leaky vessels.

Also, the habit of seeing yourself write down notes as you read will help in two other ways. Firstly, it will give you confidence, through habit, in your capacity to articulate your critical ideas in written form. You get used to seeing yourself as a critic, writing down reactions; so that inhibitions and excessive modesty begin to weaken. Critical skill only comes after you have gained the habit of regular critical utterance, no matter how raw and half-formed it may be. For once—so long as it is only for your own eyes and no one else's—let it all come freely, for good or bad. You can then, later on, read your notes, your running commentary, and begin to criticise your own criticism. To take voluminous notes on your own responses to a work, then assay them coolly, in the light of after-thought and in the light of what you have learned of other people's ideas, is one of the best forms of education. There can be no education and no insight without self-commitment (as this story of Santiago shows!).

The second way in which the note-taking habit will help to develop your skill is this. Once you begin to learn the exciting trick of submitting yourself unrestrainedly to a text yet simultaneously detaching yourself just enough to put down your thoughts in different words from the author's, then you will find yourself discovering more points than would ever have come to your mind if you had not been writing a commentary. To begin to take notes is difficult and seems artificial and mechanical. But after a while, it becomes something natural and creative in itself—a kind of flow running parallel to the text, and feeding from it and back into it all the time. The more you write, the better you read, because the two acts are profoundly dependent on one another.

Many students take notes not on an accompanying paper but on the margins and between the lines of the book they are studying. This may work well for some people, or with certain texts. But, even apart from the fact that it ruins the appearance of a book (and disfigures it for anyone else wanting to read it), it has its dangers. There is never enough room on a margin to develop your own points, and to let your pen, as it were, run away with itself. You need space in which to discover—often to your own surprise—what it is your pen can tell you that you have been capable of thinking. Also, to make notes on the actual text may make you too reliant on the words of the text—expecially when it comes to writing an examination. You must, of course, always know and remember the text as closely as possible. But to get into the habit of writing notes, or even short passages of would-be essays, on a separate paper, gives you confidence about writing criticism of a text without having the text in front of you. If you take notes in your own notebook, you are beginning to contemplate your own mind: that disconcerting blank page which slowly, then suddenly, covers itself with the marks of your independent thinking. Perhaps the end of all academic study is to learn how to contemplate the self through contemplating and analysing the words of others.

As you take notes, ask questions. Again, you will at first be oppressed by the apparent falsity of what you are doing. Why should I stop myself here, you may complain, and ask myself, What is Hemingway doing by making Santiago have cramp in one hand? Why should I risk spoiling the pleasure of the story by making myself ask, Is it bad that Santiago is made to utter these high-sounding statements about life? Or, is this appearance of the two tourists at the end just a little bit contrived, a little bit too neat? Asking yourself questions might, it is true, result in your deciding to reject certain parts of any work, or even the whole work. But it is better to reject than to accept blindly, by refusing to allow your own potential for discriminating between good and bad to come into operation. The exercise of judgement and the exercise of analysis are very closely connected; and they are fundamental activities of the mind. If you are prepared to judge a work, and form an opinion of its merits, you will find yourself learning to read critically—and a critical reading is a close reading. Students are naturally modest when it comes to criticising a work by a well-known author. And of course you should be properly cautious before coming to a judgement. But in the end it is something you cannot avoid. A reader who is always reluctant to judge a work of literature is for that reason reluctant to read fully, as a full person.

Therefore, ask questions as to the merits of what you read. And always make yourself ask interpretative questions. For example, it may at first seem natural just to accept as a reader that an old man interested in baseball should think of the sport while he is at sea, and of one prominent player, Joe DiMaggio. But if you school yourself by taking notes and by allowing the habit of questioning to sharpen your reading, you will find yourself saying, *Why* does Hemingway introduce DiMaggio at this point? What would the story lose if all references to baseball and DiMaggio were left out? (The formula of this latter question is a very useful one for making yourself discover the function and therefore the meaning of every detail you read.)

Queries. Stop at this point and try to answer this question in note-form. What *would* the story lose if Hemingway had decided to revise it so as to leave out the references to baseball and DiMaggio?

Here is another question to try to answer—a question about the value of questioning. Do *you* agree that it is important to try to form an opinion as to whether a work is good or bad?

How is the issue of critical judgement affected by the *age* of a work of literature: is it easier or harder to judge a contemporary work? Is it less or more *important* to judge a contemporary work?

Suggestions for further study

In the commentary queries have been introduced at various places, partly in order to remind the reader that what is said about the book in the Notes should not be regarded as complete, or as being above dispute. The flow of comment has been interrupted so as to remind the student that it is *his* or *her* commentary that matters in the end. There are many more issues that remain to be studied even in a work as short as *The Old Man and the Sea*. Here are some of them.

(1) Discuss in more detail the 'religious' element in the story.

Do *you* think it is appropriate or helpful to see Santiago as a Christ-figure?

Is it possible to see the story as religious in spirit, or in some general way, without identifying it with any specific religion or creed? Look carefully at the following passage:

> He had sailed for two hours, resting in the stern and sometimes chewing a bit of the meat from the marlin, trying to rest and to be strong, when he saw the first of the two sharks.
>
> *'Ay'*, he said aloud. There is no translation for this word and perhaps it is just a noise such as a man might make, involuntarily, feeling the nail go through his hands and into the wood. (p.107)

Here is one of the few occasions in the narrative where the words are clearly those of the narrator (it is similar to the 'literary' similes quoted earlier, for example where Santiago's sail, we are told, 'looked like the flag of permanent defeat'). It is certainly not always unacceptable for a narration that has been largely 'dramatic' in its narrative 'point of view'—that is, kept close to the thoughts and feelings of one or more of the characters—to have some external commentary inserted in the voice of the author. Is this present instance of change in the narrative 'point of view' successful or not?

The hint here clearly seems to be that Santiago *is* like Christ, having his hands nailed to the Cross. Do the experiences of Santiago justify Hemingway's comparison with Christ? Does Hemingway make the comparison subtly or crudely? Is it just a *hint*, or is it a *push*, by the author?

Compare the above passage with the scene near the end where Santiago climbs the road from the harbour to his shack carrying his mast. Does it seem likely that this is a veiled allusion to Christ carrying his cross to Calvary? Is there any biblical allusion in the fact that Santiago has to sit down five times on the road?

It has been suggested that when Santiago reaches his shack, and lies down on his bed, his position is that of a crucified man. Here is the passage:

> Inside the shack he leaned the mast against the wall. In the dark he found a water bottle and took a drink. Then he lay down on the bed. He pulled the blanket over his shoulders and then over his back and legs and he slept face down on the newspapers with his arms out straight and the palms of his hands up. (p.122)

Do the details of Santiago's position clearly indicate a 'crucifixion'? Does the 'atmosphere' or 'tone' of the passage, and of the writing on each side of the passage in the text, confirm that this is a solemn and near-religious moment?

And before you finish with this part of the story, here is a very small but interesting detail to consider:

> he sat there with the mast on his shoulder and looked at the road. A cat passed on the far side going about its business and the old man watched it. Then he just watched the road. (p.122)

Why does Hemingway introduce the cat? What does it add to the incident?

(2) Consider whether 'The Old Man and the Sea' can properly be regarded as a tragedy.

There is of course no agreed pattern for what constitutes a tragedy. But some features that have been expected of anything called 'tragedy' by critics in the past are these: a central hero who stands out from ordinary people; a dominant theme of suffering, physical or psychological; a strong sense of loss and of wasted powers; a 'flaw' or moral weakness in the tragic hero; an investigation of evil; a sense of 'transcendence' as well as of loss, that is, the sense that something positive and noble is achieved despite suffering and death. There are other possible features of the tragic in general: do any occur to you?

In classic tragedy, such as the *Oedipus Rex* of the Athenian dramatist Sophocles (496–406 BC) or Shakespeare's *King Lear*, the hero is outstanding: a king. Can Santiago be seen as outstanding in any comparable way, remembering that this is a modern work, written in a time when there are few kings?

Are Santiago's sufferings more physical than psychological?

Does he have a 'tragic flaw'? What do you think of the suggestion that he was guilty of 'tragic pride' in the fact that he 'went out too far' (as he himself admits, several times)? Does that make him like the tragic hero—like Melville's Ahab, say, or Faust, or Prometheus—who goes beyond the bounds of conventional knowledge, and tries to rival God or the gods? Or is this to make too much of a simple regret on Santiago's part that he has ever got involved with this particular marlin?

Are the sharks an embodiment of Evil? Can we see suffering and injustice (the loss to Santiago of all he had fought and suffered to gain) as comprising 'evil'?

And is Santiago's story one that asserts human values, through showing how they are tested and confirmed by suffering? Or does it leave the reader mainly with a sense of the futility of human effort? And can 'tragedy' leave you with such a sense?

Make comparisons at all points with any other tragedies you have read, ancient or modern.

(3) Consider the function of irony in the story.

Irony can occur in details: the tiny warbler perches delicately on the line, 'where he was more comfortable', though the line is taut with the pain of the fish and of the man joined to him. Conscious irony occurs in some of Santiago's own words: '"What an excellent fish dolphin is to eat cooked", he said. "And what a miserable fish raw."' And there are the larger-scale ironies: for example, the irony that a man comes to love the fish he is about to kill; the irony that a great and valuable catch is reduced to a mere skeleton, 'garbage waiting to go out with the tide', the irony that when the last of the fish's flesh has gone to the sharks, suddenly blood comes into the old man's mouth, 'coppery and sweet'.

Is the whole view of human existence suggested by *The Old Man and the Sea* an ironic one?

Analyse the *structure* of the story in terms of ironic contrast.

(4) Analyse several examples of Hemingway's narrative art.

For example, discuss in detail the whole episode of the sharks—how Hemingway prepares for the episode; gives a specific character to the different types of shark; stresses the kinds of weapon used by Santiago; uses pauses and moments of delusive peace or confidence; gives us a sense of Santiago's varying response to the sharks; excels in providing sensuous details and in re-creating in us the very *feel* of the combat; and so on.

Or, on a smaller scale, analyse the remembered incident of the 'hand game' between Santiago in his youth and 'the great negro from Cienfuegos'. What makes the episode so vivid? What kind of *language* does Hemingway describe it in? And why does Hemingway give us the episode at all? Is it necessary for the development and meaning of the whole story?

(5) Choose some contrasted short passages and analyse in detail Hemingway's use of language.

Consider the varied length and the construction of sentences; the importance (or unimportance) of verbs; the part played by adjectives; the rhythms of the language. Is the effect visual, or sensuous in any other way? Is it the kind of language that draws attention to itself, or is it 'transparent' and purely functional?

(6) Are there aspects of this story, or passages of it, which seem to you less successful than others?

If so, make out your case in the form of a careful argument. Avoid simple assertions or dogmatic statements. Back up any opinions you hold by illustrations from the text, and always by showing your knowledge of the story as a whole.

If it accords with your own considered judgement of the story to do so, make a defence of Hemingway against the charges that *The Old Man and the Sea* shows an immature outlook; or that its concept of human nobility is naive and over-optimistic; or that it is over-sentimental in places; or that it is too limited in its applicability to life by taking so simple an old man as its central figure; or that it is at times pretentious and inflated.

(7) Choose one other relevant short story by another author, or episode from a novel, and make a close comparison with Hemingway's style or themes or achievement.

For example, a very illuminating comparison could be made with 'The Open Boat' by Stephen Crane (1871–1900), an American novelist and short-story writer whom Hemingway admired and by whom he was certainly influenced.

Some passages from Mark Twain's *Huckleberry Finn* might provide interesting comparisons in style: particularly in the way each writer blends simple, colloquial language with language that is shaped and literary.

Passages from William Faulkner's 'The Bear' or 'The Old People', in the collection called *Go Down, Moses* by William Faulkner (1897–1962), would be valuable to compare and contrast as hunting stories, similarly touched by a tragic view of life that stresses endurance and simplicity (though the differences between the two writers are marked).

Choose an episode or a chapter from Melville's *Moby Dick* and compare the two writers' intentions and outlooks. For example, read Melville's short chapter called 'Brit' for his view of the sea, or 'the Grand Armada' for his narrative ability.

Equally productive might be a comparison with 'Youth' or 'Typhoon' by Joseph Conrad (1857–1924), another writer whom Hemingway admired.

To make short comparative studies of this kind is one of the best ways of developing your critical skills. Contrasting one writer with another is not just an empty exercise in saying 'How different!' It is a way of bringing each writer into clearer focus, and of making you modify and clarify your reading of each. It is also a way of testing your ability to discriminate and to judge. It is useful to make brief comparative references of this kind in the course of writing an essay or an answer on any one work or author: not primarily to impress by your width of reading, but in order to make your points sharper, by varying your scheme of reference.

Writing answers

There is no such thing as a satisfying 'model' answer to an examination question. Throughout the Commentary in Part 3, and in this section, the student has been encouraged to think and work creatively on his own. Specific questions have been asked for him to try to answer, or at least to think about, within the intepretation of *The Old Man and the Sea* that has been offered here. To study well is the best preparation for passing examinations.

Nevertheless, there are some further pointers that may be worth considering.

First of all, *read and understand the question.* Don't just take a quick glimpse, recognising the name 'Santiago', say, and plunging into any kind of general account of everything you can think of about Santiago. Try to think what the examiner had in mind when he set that particular question and not another. What *kind* of answer does it require? Hesitate—then, if possible, start writing some preliminary notes. A sketch outline before you start is invaluable. You can change the proposed plan of it as you go along, but it is good—good in practice and good psychologically—to start by drawing up a brief plan.

Don't plagiarise. That is, even if you wish to use the point that some critic has made about the work, since it honestly seems to you to say the last word on that particular issue, re-phrase it in your own language. Or better still, quote from the critic, giving his name and the full reference if you can; then talk *around* what the critic has said in an attempt to expand it. It is surprising how original you can become, by forcing yourself to add to or to qualify what some well-known critic has already said. *Use critics by all means, but sparingly.* It is all too easy for the student to become hypnotised by what writers of greater experience have already discovered, and to believe that there is nothing new or valid to be said about anything under the sun. Don't believe that. There are no two identical human minds on earth. And you *can* produce thoughts, interpretations, and phrases that are your own. They may not be original in a major way; but they will always be better than an undue reliance on the words and ideas of other people. An examination answer that comes entirely from second-hand sources reads mechanically. An answer that has some personal thought in it (even though not all of its ideas can ever be entirely fresh) reads very differently. An examiner, perhaps reading hundreds of answers, will be struck very forcibly by an answer that shows even a little intellectual vitality. Don't try to be too flashy or eccentric: that, too, doesn't work. But within the limits of common sense, try to follow this golden rule of writing examinations: *catch the interest of your examiner.* Make him realise that there is a mind at work behind what you write. Don't be afraid to ask questions in your answer, or to be a little tentative: that is, to say there are several possible ways of looking at something, or arguments to be expressed on both sides of the question. Show that your mind is capable of reaching out beyond safe and conventional opinions, even if only by letting yourself *wonder aloud* (as it were) as you write. That is the way in which creative minds work: they speculate, and push themselves a little beyond their previous limits. And an examiner who finds a mind trying to stretch itself in an examination answer becomes attentive and interested. A bored examiner is a hostile examiner.

Always back up your points. This can be done either by referring often to what happens in a work, or by direct quotation from the work. Don't quote too often. When you quote, quote relevantly, and never at excessive length (otherwise your examiner will suspect you of 'padding'). And it is good not just to quote and leave the quotation inert on the page without further comment from you. After you quote, single out a few significant phrases from the quotation and say something about them. That is, quotation is a useful technique in writing answers, but the quotation must be absorbed into the mental activity of what you are arguing or displaying. You must show your own mind working upon the quotation, shining new light on it, or responding to it in an interesting way.

Try to construct an argument or a 'case'. When you see a question, even one that seems fairly factual, like 'Describe the role of Manolin in *The Old Man and the Sea*', don't simply re-tell parts of the story, or amass examples without comment. You should always 'assess' and 'evaluate' within any 'description'. Describe Manolin's characteristics, by all means: his kindness, loyalty, long-standing association with Santiago, relationships with other people in the fishing community, and so on. But it is sensible to ask yourself as you are writing your answer—or, better, as you are making your preliminary outline—*is* Manolin's role so very striking? Shall I call it an interesting but minor element in the story? What different aspects are there to his role: a *structural* aspect? a *moral* aspect? even an *ironic* aspect? Do Santiago's memories of the boy help to hold the picture together, as an artistic whole? Do we see them have an effect on Santiago—for example, do they strengthen him each time? Do they highlight, by ironic contrast, the loneliness of the old man at sea? Does the thought of Manolin relate to the old man's image of *himself* when young, and therefore to his dream of Africa, and therefore to some possible theme of rediscovery or self-confirmation? Is the role of Manolin successfully handled by Hemingway? Is it always convincing that a boy and an old man should converse in the way they do, or that Manolin should have been a friend of Santiago at the age of five?

These and other questions should begin to swarm in your mind as you prepare to answer, and they should therefore ensure that you do not simply 'describe' in a flat, second-hand way, but should relate the issues of Manolin to many other things you have to say about the book. And because you are preparing to answer a question by making yourself ask related questions, you should begin to form the outline of an *argument*. Perhaps it would be like this. First, mention the few hard facts and details we know about Manolin (nothing about his appearance, a little about his family and relationships, most about the way he looks after Santiago). Then assess the boy's role in the structure of the story, including the contribution made by ironic contrast. Then the question of how Manolin brings Santiago's life into closer focus for us. Then how Manolin relates to and expresses the major themes of the book: for example, youth and age, re-birth, the initiation of youth into the facts of suffering and deprivation, confirmation of basic human values like compassion and loyalty, the need to learn practical skills as a way of coping with the uncontrollable forces of life, and so on. Then, in conclusion, perhaps this: 'It remains to be asked, Is the picture of Manolin successful in every respect?' To which you might answer, 'On the whole, yes, for the following reasons . . . However, at times Hemingway verges on the sentimental, as when we see Manolin crying at the very end', and so on.

Make the *structure and shape* of your own argument clear. Remind the reader (and yourself) of what you have just established at various points in your argument, and what you are now going on to try to establish next. That is, within sensible limits, draw attention to what you are doing, and the order you are doing it in. Write with a sense of having separate but related sections in your essay. And be prepared to divide up your material into clear categories. Even though you know very well that the categories are not watertight—for example, that in talking about Manolin's relationships you are also saying something relevant to the book's structure or to its use of irony—you should persist in using the categories as a device for getting your thoughts down on paper in a form that can be read with coherence and understanding. You can always say, as any critic must, that these categories and divisions are purely for convenience, and that in the end our grasp of the story as a whole draws all categories together, and, indeed, shows the inadequacy of clear-cut categories. Categories are like the rungs of a ladder: we need them to get up, from point to point. Once at our goal, we can leave them behind. But if we don't structure what we write in some such way, so that point follows point, each connected to the other but each noticeably different from the other, then the result can be a shapeless mass of observations and random comments. Tell the reader what you're going to do. Ask leading questions as you proceed, as signposts to the reader as well as to yourself. Make an occasional summing-up or retrospect. Use quotations sparingly but relevantly. And end with a sense of conclusion, telling the reader that *this* is the point you've been leading up to, and that it marks the goal of the whole essay.

A final point, by way of farewell. In preparing for an exam, many students come to feel that the preparation kills their imaginative enjoyment of the work. This is a real danger, and it is one you have to fight against. But *there is no necessity for preparation for an exam destroying your fresh perception and enjoyment of literature.* If you make your note-taking creative; if you make study a form of dialogue with yourself; if you continually question and experiment and challenge your own thoughts and the thoughts of your teachers or the critics you read, you can only profit from the discipline of having an exam at the end of the process. An examination ought not to be designed for parrots, but for thinking people. And it is literature itself that awaits us at the end of the process, beyond and far above examinations. Think, take notes, ask a thousand questions, write your exam answers with some style and shapeliness. Then, with your mind flexed and strengthened and made more capable of understanding and expressing itself, go back to where it all began and where it will all end: the inexhaustible mystery and delight of words and story—

> He was an old man who fished alone in a skiff in the Gulf Stream and he had gone eighty-four days now without taking a fish . . .

Part 5

Suggestions for further reading

The Text

There are hardback editions in print by Scribner's, New York, 1952, and in Great Britain by Jonathan Cape, London, 1952. There is also a paperback edition by Panther Books, St Albans, 1976.

Some other works by Hemingway

In Our Time, Boni and Liveright, New York, 1925. (Reprinted subsequently by Scribner's, New York, 1930. The selection of short stories published under the title *The Snows of Kilimanjaro*, Penguin Books, Harmondsworth, 1963, which may be more easily available, contains all but one short concluding piece of *In Our Time*: if the first two stories in the Penguin edition are omitted, the rest of the text can be taken conveniently to represent that of *In Our Time*.)

The Sun Also Rises, Scribner's, New York, 1926; published in Britain under the title *Fiesta*, Jonathan Cape, London, 1927; also published by Panther Books, St. Albans, 1976.

Men without Women, Scribner's, New York, 1927; Penguin Books, Harmondsworth, 1955.

A Farewell to Arms, Scribner's, New York, 1929; Penguin Books, Harmondsworth, 1935.

Death in the Afternoon, Scribner's, New York, 1932; Penguin Books, Harmondsworth, 1966.

Green Hills of Africa, Scribner's, New York, 1935; Penguin Books, Harmondsworth, 1966.

To Have and Have Not, Scribner's, New York, 1937; Penguin Books, Harmondsworth, 1955.

For Whom the Bell Tolls, Scribner's, New York, 1940; Penguin Books, Harmondsworth, 1955.

Across the River and into the Trees, Scribner's, New York, 1950; Penguin Books, Harmondsworth, 1966.

A Moveable Feast, Scribner's, New York, 1964; Penguin Books, Harmondsworth, 1966.

Islands in the Stream, Scribner's, New York, 1970; Penguin Books, Harmondsworth, 1972. A posthumous novel, not of very great merit, but of interest to readers of *The Old Man and the Sea* because it uses a similar setting and some similar action.

Some recommended criticism and biography

BAKER, CARLOS: *Ernest Hemingway, A Life Story*, Scribner's, New York, 1969. The standard biography, though over-detailed. Reprinted in paperback by Penguin Books, Harmondsworth, 1972.

BAKER, CARLOS: *Hemingway, The Writer as Artist*, Princeton University Press, Princeton, 1952. A major assessment, though it tends to over-interpret Hemingway's symbolism.

BAKER, CARLOS, (ED.): *Hemingway and his Critics*, Hill and Wang, New York, 1961. A useful anthology and bibliography.

BAKER, CARLOS, (ED.): *Ernest Hemingway: Critiques of Four Major Novels*, Scribner's, New York, 1962.

BAKER, SHERIDAN: *Ernest Hemingway, An Introduction and Interpretation* (American Authors and Critics Series), Holt, Rinehart and Winston, New York, 1967. A good and discriminating brief introduction.

GURKO, LEO: *Ernest Hemingway and the Pursuit of Heroism*, T.Y. Crowell, New York, 1968.

HEMINGWAY, MARY WALSH: *How It Was*, Alfred A. Knopf, New York, 1976. A biography by Hemingway's fourth wife.

JOBES, KATHERINE T. (ED.): *Twentieth Century Interpretations of The Old Man and the Sea*, Prentice-Hall, Englewood Cliffs, New Jersey, 1968.

PETERSON, RICHARD K.: *Hemingway, Direct and Oblique*, Mouton, The Hague, 1969. A good account of Hemingway's style.

ROVIT, EARL: *Ernest Hemingway*, Twayne, New York, 1963.

SANDERSON, STEWART: *Hemingway* (Writers and Critics Series), Oliver and Boyd, Edinburgh and London, 1961. One of the best general introductions.

SYLVESTER, BICKFORD: 'Hemingway's Extended Vision: *The Old Man and the Sea*', *PMLA*, LXXXI, 1966, pp.130–8.

WEEKS, ROBERT P.: *Hemingway, A Collection of Critical Essays*, Prentice-Hall, Englewood Cliffs, New Jersey, 1962.

YOUNG, PHILIP: *Ernest Hemingway: A Reconsideration*, Pennsylvania State University Press, University Park and London, 1966. A revised version of his well-known and influential critical study, *Ernest Hemingway*, published in 1952. It contains good criticism, but with emphasis on the theory of Hemingway's personal trauma.

The author of these notes

KENNETH GRAHAM is Professor of English Literature in the University of Sheffield. He is a graduate of the University of Glasgow, and the University of Oxford. He was Henry Fellow at Yale University, Assistant Lecturer in the University of Aberdeen, and Lecturer in American Literature, then in English, in the University of Southampton. He was ACLS Visiting Fellow at the University of Virginia, 1966–7; and was appointed Professor at Sheffield in 1976.

He is the author of *English Criticism of the Novel, 1865–1900*, 1965; *Tales of Edgar Allan Poe*, 1967; and *Henry James: the Drama of Fulfilment*, 1975. He has written various articles, reviews and broadcast talks on the English and American novel.